THE RAINBOW BOOK OF

American Folk Tales and Legends

THE RAINBOW BOOK

# of American Folk Tales and Legends

BY MARIA LEACH

ILLUSTRATED BY MARC SIMONT

THE WORLD PUBLISHING COMPANY

CLEVELAND AND NEW YORK

PUBLISHED BY The World Publishing Company

2231 WEST 110TH STREET, CLEVELAND 2, OHIO

PUBLISHED SIMULTANEOUSLY IN CANADA BY

NELSON, FOSTER & SCOTT LTD.

Library of Congress Catalog Card Number: 57-7405

FOR
DONALD FRIEDE

Contents

Contents

Contents

OTHER AMERICAN FOLK TALES

North American Indian

Contents

That's Folklore

HERE is a book of American folk tale and legend. More than that—here is a book of American folklore. For you cannot delve into the tales and legends and jokes and sayings of any people without discovering the people themselves—their beliefs and feelings, their life-ways and attitudes and knowledge.

That is folklore: what man has learned through the ages about the world and about himself. Folklore is not fiction; it is not baloney. When people say, "Oh, that's folklore!" meaning something untrue or unbelievable or inaccurate, they are using the term in ignorance. Yet over and over again, we hear it or see it in print.

American folklore is many things. It is tales and legends and anecdotes and jokes, songs, tunes, dances, games; it is proverbs and sayings, rimes and riddles; it is the lore of special regions and special places; it is beliefs and the wisdom that comes with living. It is all the little practices and gestures and ceremonies of daily life. It is solemn and humorous, tragic and ridiculous. It is so deeply rooted in our daily lives that we don't even know it!

This book would have to be ten books if it tried to present every phase of American folklore in any detail; therefore it is limited to a sampling of folk tales and legends. And to understand American folk tale, it is necessary to know how many kinds there are.

American folk tale includes first of all the tale from oral tradition, unwritten but remembered and retold from grandfather to father to child through the generations, until today the collectors are writing them down lest they be forgotten and lost forever. This category includes almost all the others: the tall tales, tall talk and anecdotes, the ghost stories and supernatural tales, as well as the noodle stories and jokes.

A LEGEND is a story based on fact, told as true. It centers on some actual person or place or event, but becomes elaborated or enhanced with additional incidents or an interweaving of fact and traditional or folkloristic material. There are thus the quasihistorical legends, hero, superman, and bad-man legends, local and place-name legends.

THE TALL TALE of the American backwoods and frontier is an imaginative, humorous, exaggerated narrative, so supported by circumstantial facts that the essential absurdity of it carries a real wallop. Tall tales include *yarns* (strung out and often told in the first person) and *tall talk* (short, sharp, and ending with a bang). None are exactly *lying* tales; they are a combination of fact and impossibility. In fact, this is the earmark of the tall tale: facts—facts enhanced to the nth degree. Detail and accuracy and the eyewitness note comprise the basis for the marvel. And—the tall tale has to be told deadpan, without the least flicker of amusement or unbelief on the part of the teller.

All over the country people have various names for tall tales and the telling of tall tales. They call them *lying tales, whoppers, stretchers, windies, fish stories, tough stories,* and the telling of tall tales is referred to as *pulling* or *drawing the long bow, taking the rag off the bush,* and *calling the dog.* There may be many other colorful local designations. A general term is *Munchausen tales,* because the Munchausen tales represent the type.

This book is full of tall tales. All the Paul Bunyan and Pecos Bill tales are pretty tall; so are the stories of Stormalong, John Henry, Mike Fink, Annie Christmas, and Joe Magarac; so are the state brags.

THE BAD-MAN LEGEND is an American favorite. There have been bandits and killers everywhere, but the American bad man with his six-shooter is a special breed, born of the Kansas-Missouri border warfare, trained in the cattle wars of the Plains, and perfected in the boom towns of the gold-rush era.

Every man and boy sees himself in the outlaw, identifies himself with that fearlessness, physical prowess, coolness and nerve, swift gunplay, hard riding, and the quick thinking and acting that are synonymous with the American desperado.

It is not the cold-blooded killer the people love, not the professional *gunman* who will shoot a man in the back or from hiding. It is the deadshot *gun fighter* who fights fair, the rebel against authority, especially against wealth and power abused or misused—the outlaw with a passion for justice who makes his own law, who steals from the rich and gives to the poor, who kills either in self-defense or to avenge or prevent a wrong, and who always gives his opponent an even break. This is the "good bad man," idealized and idolized. Every day he rides through some American movie or living-room TV; and his adventures and hairbreadth escapes delight readers of magazines and comic books as well.

A LOCAL LEGEND is a story that has grown up around some special place to explain some unusual but natural phenomenon. There are devil's footprints all over the world: a mark in some rock resembling a huge footprint. On Adam's Peak in Ceylon lies a rock bearing the mark of a huge footprint, and said to be the spot where Adam stood while an angel unfolded the ills of the world before his eyes. Adam's Bridge is a thirty-mile chain of little sandy islands between India and Ceylon.

Port Mouton in Nova Scotia is said to have been so named by Samuel de Champlain, the French explorer. When sailing one day along Nova Scotia's south shore, the lamb intended for dinner jumped overboard. (*Mouton* is the French word for lamb.) And there is no counting the number of rocky fields and granite formations throughout Maine, New Brunswick, and Nova Scotia pointed to as the place "where Noah dumped his ballast."

Nothing in the United States seems to be named for Adam, but the Devil has gotten around a good deal and left his mark here and there. There is Devils River in southeastern Texas, Devil's Ear Mountain in the Adirondacks, Devil's Lake in North Dakota. There is Mount Diablo in California, Diablo Canyon in Arizona, and the big Diablo dam on the Skagit River in Washington. A huge pile of hexagonal columns which look something like fenceposts in California is called the Devil's Postpile and is now a national monument. The surprising 1,200-foot rock tower on the Belle Fourche River in Wyoming is also credited to the Devil and called the Devil's Tower—another national monument.

People have come to regard the tall tale as the most typical of all American folk tales. This is because Americans love it the most. The tall tale, more than any other type, portrays the individual making light of hardship. Our pioneers either had to make light of hardship or succumb to it, and so their heroes not only surmounted obstacles and won out against odds, but achieved the impossible. Americans love the hero who is equal to anything, who stands unfazed no matter what, who makes a joke of calamity. And so it does not matter whether the tale or the legend is *factually* true, or even possible. For this invincible spirit runs through all American tall tales, whether it is Paul Bunyan easily breaking the mile-high log jam, the snowbound hunter (or the lost child) sleeping with the bear, Old Stormalong coping with the octopus, or Mary Simmons singing with the dead. So any American folk tale or legend is a true American folk tale or legend in that it embodies and reveals the spirit and stamina of the nation.

Because some tale is told as *of* a certain state does not mean that it is told in that state only. "My grandfather knew the man who . . ." is the folk tale's infallible earmark. My grandfather knew the man who heard the mosquitoes debating whether to "eat him here" or take him home to the swamp. And everybody's grandfather (in Alabama, Arkansas, Idaho, Mississippi, New Jersey, Texas) "knew the man who" heard that conversation. Wherever the story of the ghostly hitchhiker turns up it is told as a firsthand experience; but it is an old European tale which had its first American telling in 1890. The numskull story about marking the boat is one of the *Merrie Tales of the Mad Men of Gotham,* first published in England in 1560; and tellings older than that are mentioned. But in America it is told of village fools in little ports all along the Eastern seaboard. Versions are reported from South Carolina to Newfoundland, and it also turns up in lake and river districts in Arkansas, Indiana, Ontario, and other locales.

And so this book is full of things we all already know, stories all of us have already heard, in some form or other, games we have played, whoppers we have heard or cracked ourselves. And because the stories here are part and parcel of us all (without our ever having been quite aware of it) perhaps they will work a kind of alchemy to make us recognize ourselves—and each other— as American folk.

THE RAINBOW BOOK OF

American Folk Tales and Legends

YOU'VE

HEARD

ABOUT . . .

Paul Bunyan

PAUL BUNYAN was born in Maine, and one day when he was three years old he rolled downhill and felled all the trees on the hillside above the river at Wiscasset. Paul grew up to be a mighty logger. He was a huge man, and nothing stumped him. He could skin a log whole, right out of its bark, and leave the hollow casing where it lay.

The legend is that Paul was the crack A-one lumberjack in the woods of Maine, New York, Pennsylvania, westward to the forests around the Great Lakes, westward to Oregon, Washington, and British Columbia. Paul Bunyan felled his gigantic trees and performed his marvels everywhere in this country there was a forest to be logged.

Babe, the Blue Ox, the biggest ox in the world, was his constant companion. He was seven ax handles wide between the eyes, and it is sometimes said that Paul dug Lake Michigan for his water hole. Babe could haul off a whole quarter section of land (160 acres) to the place where Paul's men just sawed the trees off it "like shearing a sheep."

19

The story of Paul's breaking the log jam is one of the most famous about him. It happened up on the Wisconsin River one spring. It was such a bad jam that the logs were piled 200 feet high and were backed a whole mile upriver. No one could budge a stick of it. But when Paul and the Blue Ox arrived, Paul just said, "Stand back." He put the big ox in the river in front of the jam and then began to pepper him with rifle shot. It felt like a lot of pesky flies to Babe, and he began to switch his tail. The tail went round and round and made such a churning in the water that the river began to flow upstream. Of course, gradually the logs floated upstream with it, and the jam was broken. Then Paul called the big ox out of the river, and river and logs flowed down again as they should.

Paul's kitchen was something. The stove was twenty-four feet long and five feet wide. The cook used to bake Paul's breakfast cakes right on top of the stove, and to keep it greased they tied ham skins to the feet of an old woman who skated perpetually around the top of the stove. Some elaborations say five colored boys skating on bacon rinds kept it greased, and that it took four cooks a-baking to keep up with Paul a-eating. Once a load of peas for the camp fell into a near-by hot spring, and the men ate pea soup all winter out of the hole.

Many old folk tales have gravitated around Paul Bunyan. He was a farmer once, and an oilman, and a construction boss. He once put butter in the road ruts so he could use sleds all summer; and the tale of selling the empty well hole for postholes became at-

tached to his oil-field career. Big-mosquito stories followed him from region to region. Paul used to set traps for them, but they got loose once and carried off the cow. When they drilled through the roof, Paul just clinched their stingers with his sledgehammer. The story of the frozen lantern blazes which thawed out in the spring is told in this book under MICHIGAN (p. 105). There are no stories about the death of Paul Bunyan. He still lives.

Paul Bunyan is four things:

(1) He is the great logger—the lumberjack hero of the logging and lumber camps of America—a huge man, of superhuman strength and skill, fearless, invincible, exuberant, and the performer of exaggerated feats. The impossible never fazed him. The humor of the tales about him bespeaks the old frontier zest for a good yarn and images also the frontier gift for ridiculing and laughing off hardship and danger and death and terror. He is the great folk symbol of unfailing grit a-whistling in the dark.

(2) He is the great comic lumberjack and construction boss of the popularizers—still the superman, symbol of strength and success, but blown up into an almost burlesque personality with a good head for business.

(3) He is also the Paul Bunyan of literary usage, symbol of the bigness and strength and vitality of America, especially as treated in the works of contemporary American poets.

And (4) he is the symbol of American folklore for everyone who has ever heard his story, and for many who have undertaken to write *about* American folklore.

Many people have assumed that Paul Bunyan never was an authentic folklore figure, that he was a character invented by the lumber industry. It is true that in 1914 an ex-lumberjack named W. B. Laughead wrote an advertising booklet for the Red River Lumber Company containing a number of Paul Bunyan yarns. Nobody paid much attention to it. In 1916 he rewrote it. In 1922 he made a third try, gave the company a little pamphlet called *The Marvelous Exploits of Paul Bunyan,* and made a hit. This was an advertising pamphlet (the kind of thing now called a giveaway), and from 1922 to 1944 the Red River Lumber Company could hardly keep up with the demand for it.

But W. B. Laughead did not *make up* his stories about Paul Bunyan—at least not all of them, and perhaps none out of whole cloth. He made up the name for Babe, the Blue Ox, but he did not invent the big blue ox; and he made up some of the minor characters around Paul—Johnny Inkslinger (Paul's bookkeeper), Sam Sourdough (the cook), and others. But all camp bookkeepers were called "inkslingers," and all camp cooks were called "sourdoughs," so they too came out of tradition, in a way.

Several outstanding American folklorists (especially Daniel G. Hoffman and Herbert Halpert) have undertaken to find out whether the Paul Bunyan stories *are* or *are not* folklore, whether they ever were or were not told by the loggers and lumberjacks themselves in the woods. And they have discovered that many of the tales were told a hundred years or more before they ever became attached to the name of Paul Bunyan, and that a number of old-time lumberjacks, still living, heard the name of Paul Bunyan and the tales about him when they first went as young men into the woods—years before a word about Paul Bunyan ever appeared in print. On this and other evidence the consensus now is that the Paul Bunyan tales began to accumulate at least as early as the 1840's or 1850's.

Old Stormalong

OLD STORMALONG is the sailor's sailor and the whaler's sailor, the wonder of the American Atlantic coast, the superhero of the old days of "wooden ships and iron men." His ship was named the *Courser,* and his own name was Alfred Bulltop Stormalong. His initials, A.B.S., have been the inspiration of every American boy who ever longed to run away from home and go to sea. Able-bodied seaman is what they stand for today. Stormalong's favorite meat was shark meat, and he drank whale soup out of a dory.

Old Stormie, he was called. Old Stormie was the kind of man who would go overboard with a knife in his teeth, in the North Atlantic, just to see why the men couldn't hoist anchor. Once when this happened there was such a churning and heaving of rough water under the ship that even the old hands got seasick. After this had gone on for fifteen minutes Old Stormie popped his head up and yelled, "Haul 'er in, boys."

So the sailors hoisted the anchor, and when Old Stormalong climbed aboard he explained, "Octopus. Four arms grabbin' the anchor, four arms grabbin' the bottom."

"What you do to him?" the sailors asked.

"Nothin' much," said Stormalong. "Just tied up all his arms in double carrick bends. Take 'im a month to get the knots out."

The *Courser* was so big she couldn't sail up Boston Harbor, so big that all the men on watch had to ride horseback. Her mast tips disappeared into the clouds and were hinged so they could be lowered to let the sun and moon go by. She was a deep-water ship, all right. No harbor in the world could take her. Old Stormalong himself was the only man strong enough to handle the wheel.

The only time the *Courser* ever went through the English Channel, Stormalong ordered the men to soap the sides. She slipped through, all right, but it was such a tight squeeze the cliffs of Dover scraped all the soap off her starboard side; they have been white ever since. The surf there is still sort of sudsy, too.

Once the *Courser* got out of hand in a storm during a September hurricane in the Caribbean. Old Stormalong had no fears for his ship, but he was scared stiff it might knock into one of the little islands and tear it up by the roots. It was some storm, though, that sent the *Courser* the whole length of the Gulf of Mexico and tearing right through the Isthmus of Panama. The next morning there she rode, calm as silk, in the Pacific Ocean. The U. S. government had sent a whole crew of Army engineers down there to build a canal; and of course they say the engineers did it. No such thing. It was Old Stormalong in the *Courser*.

Some people say Old Stormalong was buried at sea off Cape Horn, wrapped in a silver shroud and lowered with a golden chain. But the common belief is that he is buried on the seashore somewhere between Maine and Florida. No one knows the exact spot, but it is somewhere where the salt spray wets his grave.

Pecos Bill

WHO invented western movies? Pecos Bill. He invented the lasso, too; he invented roping and the six-shooter. He taught the broncos how to buck and then taught the cowboys how to ride the broncos. Pecos Bill is the great cowboy hero of the Southwest, and his story has traveled to the cowboys of the Argentine and is told even in Australia. He could rope anything, they say—bears, buffalo. He used to throw his loop straight up and rope down buzzards out of the sky. Once he even roped a train and nearly wrecked it. "Pecos Bill could rope a streak of lightning": that is his legend.

Pecos Bill was born in east Texas (about 1832, some say) of pioneer parents who felt that Texas was getting too crowded when another family moved in fifty miles away. So one day they packed up the wagon and headed west. The day they crossed the Pecos River, young Bill fell out of the wagon. There were so many children in the family that nobody missed the baby, and when they did it was too late to go back.

But young Bill fell in with some coyotes and they brought him up. He always thought he was a coyote himself until one day a cowboy found him, stark naked eating bear meat, and told him he wasn't. Bill couldn't believe it.

"But I got fleas," he argued, "and I howl at night—howl good, too."

"All Texans got fleas," said the cowboy. "Besides, where's your tail?"

Bill looked. He had no tail.

"I never noticed that," he said. "All right, I'll go human." So he went along with the cowboy, and after that Pecos Bill was a cowboy.

After he had killed off all the bad men in Texas, he got restless and bored, and headed west, "looking for a hard outfit," he said. On the way his horse broke a leg, and Bill had to continue the trip on foot. But when he finally got where he was going, he was riding a mountain lion and swinging a rattlesnake in loops.

Pecos Bill staked out New Mexico and fenced in Arizona, and one summer in drought time he dug the Rio Grande. He had a famous horse named Widow Maker (no other man who ever tried to ride him lived) and a dog named Norther, who could run down a buffalo and hang onto its ear till Bill came along and skinned it.

Bill's wife was named Sluefoot Sue. She was a wonderful rider herself. In fact Bill fell in love with her because she could ride anything from a fish to the toughest horse on the range. But Sluefoot Sue couldn't rest until she had ridden Widow Maker. Bill tried to stop her, but she did it anyway. She was all dressed up in her wedding dress over a fine pair of steel-spring bustles.

Of course Widow Maker pitched her off first thing. Sluefoot Sue landed on the bustles and began to bounce. She bounced—and bounced—and bounced—and nothing could stop her. Pecos Bill was heartbroken over his bouncing bride. Finally, after she had bounced for three days and four nights, in the mercy of his heart he pulled out his six-shooter and shot her to keep her from starving to death.

There are several stories about the death of Pecos Bill. One says he drank himself to death, washing down barbed wire with nitro-glycerin. Another says he walked into Cheyenne, Wyoming, the day they put on the first rodeo and died of nostalgia for the good old days. And another says the day a man from Boston turned up at the ranch wearing a mail-order cowboy outfit, Bill just lay down and laughed himself to death.

27

Johnny Appleseed

JOHNNY APPLESEED: pioneer, wandering apple-seed sower, and orchardist of the Middle West. He is usually depicted dressed in a coffee-sack shirt with a hole cut in it for his head, an upside-down mush-kettle hat over shoulder-length hair, and barefoot. In folk narrative he is always about sixty-eight years old, with a long gray beard—saintly, eccentric, penniless, benevolent.

The heart of his legend is that he spent forty years wandering through Ohio and Indiana planting apple orchards. He would clear an acre or so of ground in the wilderness, plant his seeds, build a brush fence around the clearing, and travel on, twenty miles or so, and plant another spot. Later he would return and care for his seedlings and young trees, sell or give them to new settlers, and teach the newcomers how to care for them. How basically the frontier people *needed* apples in their meager diet would make a long story in itself.

Johnny Appleseed lived nowhere—except in crude lean-to camps of elm poles and bark while he was doing his felling and clearing and planting. But often in his travels he would stop overnight in some settler's cabin and bring the people "news fresh from heaven." He would lie on his side on the floor and read to them, by flickering firelight, out of the Bible or from the works of Swedenborg.

Johnny Appleseed was a real person. His name was John Chapman. He probably never did wear a coffee-sack shirt or a mush-kettle hat. He was not just a religious old tramp who went around planting apple seeds and giving away every cent he got. He did not plant every "first orchard" in Connecticut, Massachusetts, Vermont, New York, Pennsylvania, Maryland, Virginia, Kentucky, Tennessee, West Virginia, Missouri, Nebraska, Arkansas, Wisconsin, or Iowa, nor in any of the Rocky Mountain States, nor anywhere on the Pacific Coast. He was not a saintly graybeard *all his life!* He was not penniless, either. In fact, when this "penniless tramp" died he owned one town lot and twenty-two pieces of good farm land in Ohio and Indiana, totaling 1,200 acres. And he never went west to Pittsburgh on the front seat of a covered wagon, as many a story tells.

The true story is better than the myth. He was a much huskier, tougher character than the pretty tales make out. He did wear shoulder-length hair; so did all frontier woodsmen—for warmth in the bitter frontier winters. And he did go barefoot. Shoes would wear out and were hard to come by. It was more practical for a wandering man to be *able* to do without them. Johnny Appleseed walked barefoot through the forests until his feet were so tough he could walk on ice without minding. He used to stick needles and pins into the toughened soles to amuse little children when he stopped overnight at frontier cabins.

John Chapman was born at Leominster, Massachusetts, September 26, 1774, and died an old man, seventy-one years old, in the cabin of his friends the Worths, north of Fort Wayne, Indiana, in March, 1845. In the cold, rainy, snowy first half of March that year, Johnny Appleseed received news that some cattle had broken into his apple nursery on the St. Joseph River near Fort Wayne. The old man set out at once, for this orchard was large and one of the

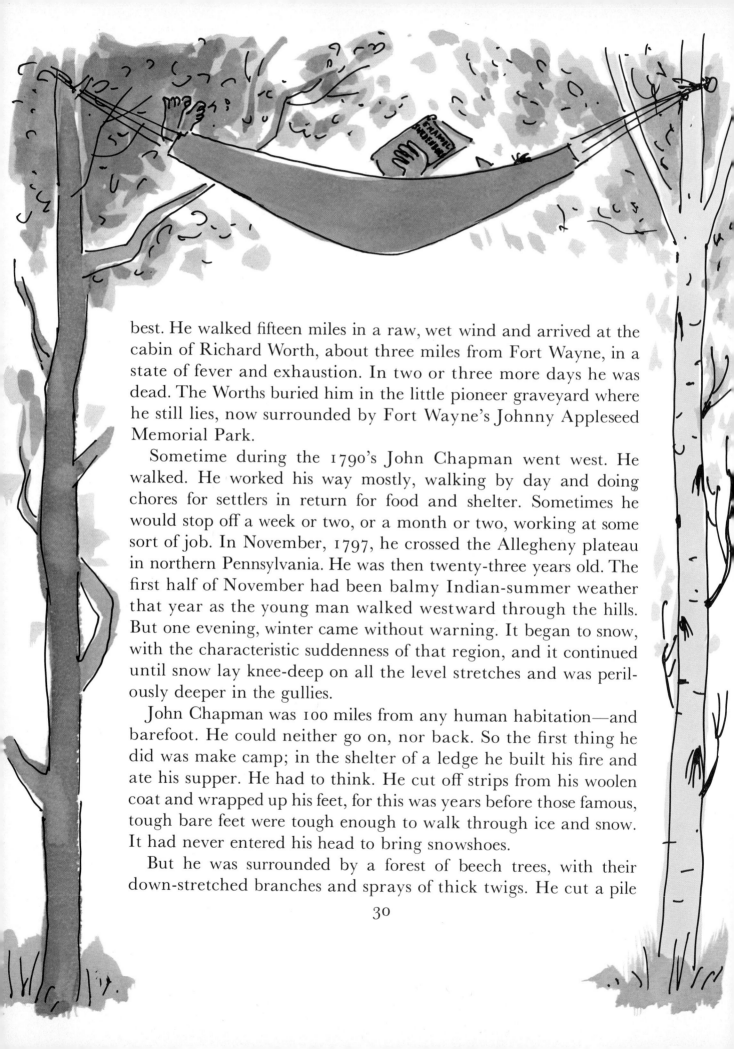

best. He walked fifteen miles in a raw, wet wind and arrived at the cabin of Richard Worth, about three miles from Fort Wayne, in a state of fever and exhaustion. In two or three more days he was dead. The Worths buried him in the little pioneer graveyard where he still lies, now surrounded by Fort Wayne's Johnny Appleseed Memorial Park.

Sometime during the 1790's John Chapman went west. He walked. He worked his way mostly, walking by day and doing chores for settlers in return for food and shelter. Sometimes he would stop off a week or two, or a month or two, working at some sort of job. In November, 1797, he crossed the Allegheny plateau in northern Pennsylvania. He was then twenty-three years old. The first half of November had been balmy Indian-summer weather that year as the young man walked westward through the hills. But one evening, winter came without warning. It began to snow, with the characteristic suddenness of that region, and it continued until snow lay knee-deep on all the level stretches and was perilously deeper in the gullies.

John Chapman was 100 miles from any human habitation—and barefoot. He could neither go on, nor back. So the first thing he did was make camp; in the shelter of a ledge he built his fire and ate his supper. He had to think. He cut off strips from his woolen coat and wrapped up his feet, for this was years before those famous, tough bare feet were tough enough to walk through ice and snow. It had never entered his head to bring snowshoes.

But he was surrounded by a forest of beech trees, with their down-stretched branches and sprays of thick twigs. He cut a pile

30

of these and set himself to working with them, heating them at his fire until they were soft and workable. First he bent two tough long, slender branches into oval snowshoe frames and tied the ends with moosewood stems. This shrub is also called leatherwood because its tough, pliant stems can be used like leather thongs. He wove the inner web with beech twigs, and after much labor completed a pair of snowshoes that would do. He tied them to his feet with the moosewood thongs and continued his journey. In two more weeks, about December 1, he knocked on the door of a dwelling near Warren, Ohio. Here he told his tale and spent the winter.

He had brought apple seeds with him in his knapsack, and in the spring he planted them. He chose a lovely river spot, six miles south of Warren, on the banks of the Big Brokenstraw. This was the first recorded apple-planting out of the many, many credited to Johnny Appleseed in the next forty years.

Johnny Appleseed stories were scattered, like his apple seeds, all through the unbroken wilderness between the Allegheny River and the Wabash. And he told them *himself,* before little log-cabin fires, to the isolated settlers who took him in. He told about hairbreadth escapes from flood or drowning in turbulent rivers, of being snowbound all winter on some river island and surviving on butternuts, of floating 100 miles down the Allegheny River asleep in his canoe, perched on a huge ice cake, or of planting a new orchard in some wild river place, or sleeping with a bear for warmth.

Johnny Appleseed's reputation for strangeness probably arose from three things: (1) his makeshift garb (for he dressed in an odd assortment of castoff clothing given him by others); (2) his tenderness for animals (mercy toward wild animals met only with laughter in that merciless frontier environment); and (3) his preaching the doctrines of Swedenborg.

There are stories that he would never take all the honey from a bee tree; he would take only what he needed and leave ample for the bees themselves. Once he told about romping with twin bear cubs while the mother looked on. Once he set a wolf free from a cruel trap and doctored its injuries; it followed him for years like a dog. He would not even kill a rattlesnake. The Indians never

31

killed snakes, he would say, and they never attack a man unless attacked themselves. "If you talk to it, it will go away," he said.

He had a special great compassion for old broken-down horses. It was the custom in those days when a horse had outlived its usefulness to turn it loose in the forest to die or survive by itself. Every year as winter neared, Johnny Appleseed would go around and collect these old animals and bargain with this settler and that to keep one over until spring. In the spring he collected them again and led them to lush pasture. Many of them regained health and value, but he would never sell one. Sometimes he would lend one, or even give one away, but never again would he leave one to the mercy of a practical man.

While wandering, Johnny Appleseed sometimes slept in a hammock slung high in the air between the tops of two trees. There are stories of woodsmen coming upon him thus, asleep or reading in his airy bed.

One of the most famous stories about Johnny Appleseed is of his saving the people of Mansfield, Ohio, from Indian massacre in the War of 1812. He ran twenty-six miles through the forest to Mt. Vernon for help and returned in twenty-four hours.

Johnny Appleseed turns up in yearly local pageants, in novels, drama, poetry, in children's books, on radio and TV programs, in the movies, and in a piece of sculpture shown at the New York World's Fair in 1939. There is a Johnny Appleseed cantata, a Johnny Appleseed operetta for children, and a Johnny Appleseed chorus for mixed voices. Johnny Appleseed Week, the last week in September, has been celebrated in Ohio since 1941. And there are at least ten Johnny Appleseed memorials: a granite marker at his birthplace in Leominster, Massachusetts, and a monument in Springfield; two monuments in Ashland, Ohio, one in Dexter City, and one in Mansfield, Ohio; and three in Fort Wayne, Indiana (the Johnny Appleseed Memorial Bridge over the St. Joseph River, Johnny Appleseed Memorial Park, where he is buried, and a granite boulder in Swinney Park). The Johnny Appleseed Memorial Highway runs from Pomeroy to Toledo, Ohio.

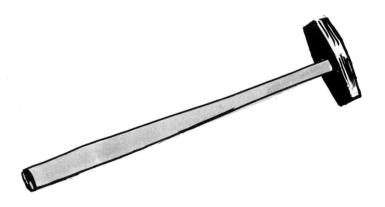

John Henry

JOHN HENRY was a steel-drivin' man: famous Negro strong man and work hero, known and talked about and bragged about and yarned about and sung about in every Negro work camp, construction gang, and levee camp in the South. And he died with his hammer in his hand: the twelve-pound hammer (some say twenty) that flashed like gold when he swung it. The women used to come out from town when John Henry worked to hear John Henry sing and the hammer ring.

John Henry was probably a real person, but so much legend has grown up around his prowess that it is hard to be sure. He was born in Tennessee (Mississippi also claims the honor) and was thirty-four years old when he died. He was a big man—220 pounds.

The John Henry story begins in the early 1870's when the Big Bend Tunnel of the Chesapeake and Ohio Railroad was being built nine miles east of Hilton in the West Virginia hills. John Henry had prodigious strength and a prodigious work record. He could drive steel ten hours without stopping. He could drive his drill into solid rock and shake down mountains. They say he took sick one

day, and his wife went to work in his place: pretty Polly Ann, drivin' steel like a man. (Some say her name was Lucy Ann, and some say Pauline.)

One day the boss bought a steam drill to hurry the work in the tunnel. John Henry's pride was touched. "A man ain't nothin' but a man," he said. "But before I let that steam drill beat me down, I'm gonna die with the hammer in my hand." And he did. John Henry raced the newfangled contraption—and won. But he died of it.

John Henry was driving on the right side of the tunnel, and the steam drill started on the left. The conditions of the race were that they would drill for thirty-five minutes. John Henry made fourteen feet, and the steam drill "it made only nine." John Henry said, "I beat 'im but I'm dead," and he burst his heart and fell down dead. And he still had the hammer in his hand. They buried him right there in the sand beside the track, and every big engine that goes by whistles, "There lies the steel-drivin' man."

There are fifty versions of the John Henry ballad and an unknown number of John Henry hammer songs to whose rhythm workmen still drive steel into solid rock. One of them goes:

> This old hammer kill John Henry
> Drivin' steel, drivin' steel
>   or
> This old hammer kill John Henry
> Can't kill me, can't kill me.

Daniel's Dear

DANIEL BOONE is usually associated with Kentucky; he was the Kentucky pioneer hero par excellence. But he was born in Berks County, Pennsylvania, in 1735, and moved with his father and family at the age of eighteen to a holding on the Yadkin River in North Carolina. Here he continued to range the woods and became the crack shot and fearless hunter the stories tell about.

One night Daniel was out with a friend on a fire hunt. This means they carried fire in a pan to dazzle and blind a deer so they could shoot him between the eyes as he stood dazed and staring at the blaze. They were creeping cautiously through a hazel thicket when Daniel suddenly gave the signal to stop; he had "shined the eyes" of a deer. He thought they looked blue, but he could not tell for sure, and anyway deer do not have blue eyes!

He raised his rifle and took aim, but the deer was off with a leap, crashing through the underbrush. Daniel chased after it as hard as

36

he could go, but the deer was faster. It headed toward Farmer Bryan's place and vaulted over the fence into the farmyard. The dogs set up a ferocious ki-yi, and Daniel continued his pursuit.

When he arrived at Farmer Bryan's place he was immediately set upon by four big dogs—and no deer in sight.

"A pet deer, maybe," he thought to himself, for frontier children often gentled some fawn, which would hang around the farm for food and petting and would be protected by the farm dogs.

So Daniel decided to inquire. He knocked on the door and was welcomed in by Farmer Bryan. Just as he entered the room a young girl about sixteen years old rushed in, panting, through another door.

"Oh, Father," she cried, "I was down to the creek setting my lines, and a panther chased me!"

Thus the panther and the deer were introduced and fell in love at first sight. This is how Daniel Boone met Rebecca Bryan, who soon afterward became Rebecca Boone.

Neither of them knew it that night, but Rebecca Boone was to be the very first woman to go to Kentucky.

Davy Crockett

"THERE must be something in me that attracts attention," Davy said, although he claimed not to know what it was. But that something is the reason why the real Davy Crockett still survives the many mediocre books about him and periodic commercial exploitations of his name. Truth is always more exciting than fiction. As he said, "It's the grit in a fellow that makes the man." And where there is enough grit nothing can obliterate the man.

American children themselves have helped to debunk the misrepresentations of Davy Crockett. In some books, he killed his first bear when he was three, or six, or eight; children, with their burlesque rimes and healthy scorn of phony precocity, sing:

> Davy Crockett—born in Tennessee
> Was killed in a bar at the age of three.

No mountain top—no bear—evidently nothing but his just deserts.

Davy Crockett, American frontier hero, is famous as a woodsman, crack marksman and sharpshooter, Indian fighter (in the War of 1812 under Andrew Jackson against the Creeks), bear hunter, bragger, joker, political campaigner, congressman, champion of the settler against land speculators, hero and martyr of the Alamo. He was fearless and tireless; he had great physical strength —and courage, great courage. All this, against the backdrop of frontier hardship and hazard, unlettered frontier common sense, trickery, and grim wit makes the legend.

The legend was augmented in the early nineteenth century by a score or more of comic almanacs which swept across the country from the West even into New England. Especially after Crockett's death at the Alamo (1836) the people took his prowess and proverbs to themselves and built a structure of tall tales and tall talk, practical jokes, and comic exploits that went off on a far tangent from those of the skilled hunter and hero of the frontier and the earnest young congressman who wanted to save the land from the speculators. These almanac tales ran the gamut from the ridiculous to the poetic: from wringing the tail off Halley's comet and climbing Niagara Falls astride an alligator (who walked up it "as slick as a wildcat up a white oak") to the famous frozen sunrise story.

This is a tale of one cold winter morning when "the very daybreak froze fast as it was trying to dawn." The earth "friz fast on her axes and couldn't turn round," and the sun was "jammed between two cakes of ice." Davy knew something had to be done or all creation would freeze over, and that would be the end of the world. Fortunately he happened to have a fresh-killed bear on his back, so he beat the carcass against the ice until the hot oil began to pour out of it. With this, Davy thawed the sun's axes, gave the works a kick, and sun and earth resumed their eternal round. Then he lighted his pipe by the sun-blaze, shouldered his bear, and walked home "with a piece of sunrise in his pocket."

But the extravagant stories and "tarnatious," "whangslanger" language of the almanacs (that out-Crocketted Crockett) gradually slipped out of popular memory. The almanacs got kicked around and lost and are now hard to find.

David Crockett was born in Tennessee "far back in the woods . . . , on the banks of the Nolachunky River," he says in his own story, on August 17, 1786. He was the fifth son in a family of six sons and three daughters. He always wished he had been the seventh son, he says, because then he would have been a doctor. This may sound strange to modern city ears, but in other days, in France and the British Isles and throughout America, a seventh son was said to be born with healing powers and an innate knowledge of curing herbs. The belief still turns up once in a while today in isolated rural sections of this country.

There are so many Davy Crockett stories that it would be hard to pick out any "most famous" one, but he is perhaps *the* most widely sung of all frontier bear hunters. He was famous as a bear hunter in a region where bear-hunting was a major activity, bear meat a prime dish, and where conversation at any social get-together began with the words, "Did you get your bear?"

Davy was in his teens, obviously, when he killed his first bear, and still in his teens, by all estimates, when he wrestled with one. His autobiography makes no mention of any dog named Whirlwind. When he went bear-hunting he took along "two good dogs and an old hound," and he says they all helped. Later he had eight big fierce dogs, killed 105 bears in one season, and was elected to the Tennessee legislature on the strength of it. Davy Crockett is probably the only legislator this country ever had who was elected for that reason.

The story of grinning the coon down out of the tree is based on a remark Davy Crockett made about himself. He claimed he was "ugly enough to grin the bark off a tree," but the way he told it on himself was that one moonlight night he tried to grin a coon down out of a tree. He grinned and grinned, but it never came down. When daybreak came he saw it was not a coon at all he was grinning at; it was a big gnarl on the tree—but he *had* grinned the bark off that!

No summary of the Davy Crockett legend would be complete without the trading-the-coonskin story. This was an episode of 1827, a year Davy Crockett was running for Congress. In the midst of one of his stump speeches the crowd began to complain that it

was a dry subject, they needed drinks, and Davy must treat them. When they entered the "shantee" (the bar)—Davy in the lead of a singing crowd—he was refused a quart of rum because he could not pay ready cash. His popularity was at stake; he knew that well enough. So he struck off into the woods with his rifle. In fifteen minutes he had shot a coon, skinned it, and returned to the shantee with his crowd. A coonskin was the same as money in those days and was accepted instantly.

In the middle of Davy's next speech, the voters got thirsty again. Davy was thinking he would have to shoot another coon, but as they entered the shantee his eye happened to fall on the coonskin sticking out between the logs of the bar. He gave it a jerk and found it in his hand, slapped it on the counter, and treated his friends again—and again—and again—by the same trick—ten times before the day was over.

"This joke secured me my election," Davy reports, for the voters allowed that anyone that clever "was the real grit for them in Congress," and his opponent might just as well have "whistled jigs to a milestone." This was also the trick that earned Davy Crockett the epithet of "coonskin congressman."

In Washington, when Congress convened, he introduced himself to his colleagues with the famous half-horse, half-alligator speech:

"I am that same Davy Crockett, fresh from the back woods, half-horse, half-alligator, a little touched with the snapping turtle. . . . I can whip my weight in wildcats . . . and eat any man opposed to Jackson."

David Crockett served three terms in Congress, but his eventual opposition to Jackson lost him the re-election in 1834, and he decided to head for Texas. "I promised to give the Texians a helping hand on the highroad to freedom," Davy wrote in 1835, ". . . for if there is anything in this world particularly worth living for, it is freedom."

The rest of the story is in every history book in the United States: the battle of the Alamo. There Davy Crockett fought and died, hero and martyr of the Alamo.

Mike Fink

SNAPPING TURTLE of the Ohio: that was Mike Fink. Ring-tailed roarer: that was Mike, too. Born with the alligators, so he said: a man of the half-horse, half-alligator breed. That was Mike Fink: the last of the amazing keelboatmen of the Ohio and Mississippi rivers; noisy, uproarious, tough; fighter, drinker, bragger, practical joker; completely fearless, often cruel; strong man and dead shot. He could drive a nail with a bullet. He would fight any man who failed to laugh at his jokes, and he could lick any bully on the rivers with one hand tied behind him. A ring-tailed roarer, for sure.

A "ring-tailed roarer" was an American frontiersman who bragged of being dangerous, fearless, and full of deeds. If he did no more than brag, and could not or did not live up to his bragging, he was known for a weakling and called a "screamer."

Mike Fink was a real person; he was born in 1770 at old Fort Pitt (now Pittsburgh), Pennsylvania. He had his first rifle at twelve and fought Indians at thirteen. The day he said his first cuss word, he shot a running squirrel through the eye. He was an Indian

scout at seventeen on the northwestern Pennsylvania border, and there his reputation for marksmanship and daring grew apace.

In the early 1800's, river-boat life lured him to the calling of keelboatman, and for the next twenty years or so Mike Fink earned his reputation for strength and skill and endurance and daring by propelling keelboats over 1,500 miles of rivers full of whirlpools, sandbars, mud banks, and snags. His spare time was spent shooting, fighting, bragging, brawling, thus earning the rest of his reputation.

River fights were barehanded fights, which began with infuriating taunts and ended with gouged-out eyes, stomped-in ribs or stomachs, mutilation, death. "King of the keelboatmen," Mike Fink was called, for his strength and accomplishment; "king of the

44

river brawlers," he was called, too, and was entitled to wear a red turkey feather in his hat because he licked them all.

The Mississippi River keelboats were 50 to 70 feet long, 14 to 18 feet wide. The cargo box in the middle was four feet deep in the hold, and the freight was piled four or five feet over that, under a curved roof which shed rain. But the big Ohio River keelboats were 70 to 100 feet long, 20 to 25 feet wide, and sometimes carried as much as seventy tons of freight. There was an 8- to 10-foot deck at each end and an 18-inch catwalk along each side. The round trip between Pittsburgh and Cincinnati took a month. The old keelboats floated downstream and bushwhacked back (the crew worked them upstream against the current by sheer strength, pulling on the bushes and trees along the bank). Some of them

45

poled upstream, however (it took twenty men to pole a keelboat), and sometimes the men walked the banks and towed the keelboat with a rope.

Mike Fink was five feet ten inches tall, black-haired, black-eyed. His typical trapping garb was a red shirt under a blue capote with white fringe. He wore moccasins and a wide leather belt in which he carried a knife. His keelboat garb was nothing but a pair of pants in summer, furs from head to heel in winter.

He was shooting bears and Indians the same time Davy Crockett was. And unlike most of our American folk heroes, these two once met. They met one day in the woods when both were hunting, and that night Davy Crockett slept on a blanket on the floor of Mike's cabin. The first thing Mike said in the morning was, "I've got the handsomest wife, the fastest horse, and the best rifle of any man in the country!" Davy Crockett admitted that Mike's wife was a handsome woman, all right; and he didn't even have a horse, so he didn't bother to brag about its speed. But Davy never left a dare hanging in mid-air when it came to shooting with a rifle.

He saw a cat sitting on the top rail of the fence around Mike's potato patch, took aim, shot the hair clean off the top of its head, same as a razor, and both its ears. The old cat never even missed them till he started to scratch!

Mike saw at once that Davy was right up in his class; but not to be outdone, he took aim at an old sow with a litter of pigs way off in the next field. He started firing, and in a minute not one of the pigs had a tail on it.

"Shoot the tails back on again, Davy!" said Mike.

"Can't do that," said Davy, "but I'll neaten 'em up a bit."

So Davy Crockett took aim at one little pig that had about one inch of tail left on it, and with one shot he took it off even, like the others.

It was easy to see they were equals with a rifle. Mike looked around for some new target to prove his skill, and saw his wife walking across the field to the spring to get water. Almost without aiming he shot half the comb out of her hair without messing it up. Then he yelled to her to stand still and let Davy hit the other half. She stopped in the path, grinning pleasantly, for she was used to this kind of foolishness. But Davy Crockett refused to shoot at a woman. So that settled that.

As steamboats gradually took the place of keelboats, the wild river roarers began to look for new space to roar in. In 1822 Mike Fink joined the Mountain Fur Company at Fort Henry, Montana, near the mouth of the Yellowstone River, and became part of the hunting, trapping, trading life in the Rockies.

Part of the fun of this life was shooting a can or a tin cup off the head of a pal. This performance proved two things: marksmanship and friendship. In fact, it was called the "ritual of friendship," because it took a heap of friendship and trust to let a man try it.

Mike Fink was an expert at this, and he and his young friend Carpenter proved their marksmanship and friendship every day— until one fatal day when Mike killed Carpenter.

There have been many versions of this final episode in Mike Fink's life, and many speculations. Was it an accident? Or did Mike mean to kill Carpenter?

It happened at a big gathering—a spring celebration—full of brag and tall talk and fancy shooting and the usual shooting of tin cups off heads. Young Carpenter shot first and knocked the tin cup off Mike's head, but the bullet accidentally grazed Mike's scalp. Mike in turn took aim at the cup on Carpenter's head and shot him between the eyes. For the rest of his life Mike went around protesting and declaring it was an accident. But many people secretly thought that Mike was too good a shot for it to *be* an accident. Sometime later, a man named Talbott, a friend of Carpenter's, met Mike in a tavern, and in the midst of one of Mike's protestations, shot him dead.

There is a movement on foot today to bring Mike Fink's body back to Pennsylvania. The Old Boatman's Association wants to move it from its grave at the mouth of the Yellowstone River where Mike has lain since 1823, and rebury him in the grounds of Henry Bouquet's Redoubt at Pittsburgh, where Mike was born.

Annie Christmas

ANNIE CHRISTMAS was a keelboat pilot on the lower Mississippi, a strong woman and bully killer. Just let her hear a man say, "I'm the bully of the town!" and he never said it again. She was six feet eight inches tall in her bare feet, and weighed 250 pounds. Her mustache was blond and curled, the finest and widest on the river. She always clipped it short and neat before a fight, though, so no one could get a good hold. Sometimes she put on pants and worked on the levee, but mostly she kept to the boats.

48

Annie was a three-barrel flatboat unloader. She could walk a gangplank with a barrel of flour under each arm and one on her head. Once in a fit of impatience she towed a keelboat all the way from New Orleans to Natchez, ". . . and it sure skimmed along fast," the people said. "As strong as Annie Christmas" was a saying in the river towns.

Annie was a wonderful fighter. She could lick any bully on the river (and did). She too had the right to wear the red turkey feather in her hat which was the badge of honor of the river champions. She even scared Mike Fink off the lower Mississippi; if he ever showed up down there, she said, she'd pole him home lashed to the bottom of a keelboat. She would have, too.

Her necklace was something to tell tales about. Annie had a bead necklace which she wore to parties. Every bead in it represented an eye she'd gouged out in a fight, or an ear or a nose she had chawed off. When she died, the necklace was thirty feet long—a true memento—and it could have been longer, only some of the fights were so easy Annie didn't feel it was honorable to record them.

Annie fell in love once with a gambling man named Charlie. She loved him dearly because of his elegant waistcoats. They got married finally, and Annie had twelve sons, all born at once, and every one of them grew to be seven feet tall. Charlie got killed in a gambling game one night, but won it just the same. Annie grieved for Charlie's death tremendously. Nothing could comfort her. She gave him a grand big funeral with his winnings, then went home and put on her best dress and her beads and shot herself.

The twelve big sons put on their twelve black coats and walked into town and bought a big black coffin. They hired a black hearse with twelve black horses and lifted the black coffin into it. Then the sons lined up, six on each side, and walked slowly with the hearse to the river. They put the coal-black coffin on the coal-black barge. In the dark of the moon they cut the black ropes that moored it, stepped on board, and floated down the river. The people stood on the levees singing in the dark as the barge floated by, down the river and out to sea. This was the end of Annie Christmas.

Casey Jones

CASEY JONES is the great American railroad engineer hero who would not save his own life but died in the performance of duty. Casey was engineer of the Illinois Central's crack train *Cannonball,* which ran between Memphis, Tennessee, and Canton, Mississippi. He was skillful and fearless and always brought the train in on time. He was skillful with the whistle too—the locomotive whistle. He had a special way of blowing it: beginning very softly, rising to a shriek, and dying away. It would make people's hair stand on end in their beds as the train whooshed by in the night. "There goes Casey," they would say.

Casey's real name was John Luther Jones. He was born at Jordan, Kentucky, in 1864, and when still in his teens moved to Cayce, Kentucky. His nickname was for his home town, Cayce (pronounced Casey). He went to work for the Illinois Central Railroad as a fireman in 1888 and was a full-fledged engineer by 1890.

On the night of April 29, 1900, when Casey had just finished his own run and brought the *Cannonball* into Memphis on time, he learned that the engineer of another engine was ill and could not make his run. Casey volunteered to make the run for his friend and pulled the big eight-wheeler out of Memphis at 11 P.M., already one hour and thirty-five minutes late at the start.

Casey was determined to make up the time. He opened the throttle wide and "balled the jack." "Jack" is railroad slang for locomotive; "ball" is short for "highball," which is the railroad signal to go ahead. To highball means not only to go ahead, but to go fast, to risk everything to get there. Newspaper accounts the next day said that Casey Jones died "highballing No. 382 out of Memphis."

By four o'clock in the morning he had made up most of the time and might have made up all of it, but ahead of him, suddenly, as he rounded a curve near Vaughan, Mississippi, he saw a stalled freight train on the track.

"Jump, Sim," he cried.

Sim Webb, fireman to Casey Jones, jumped and lived to tell the story. Casey's body was found in the wreckage with one hand still on the whistle cord and one on the air-brake lever.

The Casey Jones ballad, by Wallace Saunders, his worshipping Negro engine wiper, has made the engineer hero immortal. The traditional song, words and melody, as sung by Saunders from the heart, made an instant hit with all who heard it. A popularized version made the vaudeville circuits and the sheet-music and record markets a few years later.

During World War I American soldiers sang the song in France; the American Army of Occupation took it into Germany. And the people took it up with enthusiasm. *Casey Jones! il monte à la cabane* sang the French. *Casey Jones! er stieg die Hutte* shouted the young Germans. Now the song is popular in South Africa. *Casey Jones! En begonzijn laatste reis naar 't belooofte land* is the way South African Dutch railroad workers sing it.

There are fourteen different versions of "Casey Jones" preserved on records in the Archives of American Folksong in the Library of Congress. There are traditional, popular, French, German, Italian, and South African Dutch versions; there are several Southern

51

Negro versions, a construction-gang version, a hobo version, a section-gang version, even an I.W.W. (the Industrial Workers of the World) version.

As time passes, the brave American engineer takes deeper and deeper hold on the American imagination. There is a monument to Casey Jones in Cayce, Kentucky. In 1950 the United States government issued a commemorative three-cent stamp in honor of American railroad engineers, which bears the portrait of Casey Jones and a picture of old Engine #382.

53

Joe Magarac

JOE MAGARAC is the strong-man hero of the steel mills of
western Pennsylvania, the idealized Hungarian steelworker
dedicated to the work. He was born inside an ore mountain.
The steelworkers themselves never heard of him until one Fourth of
July picnic when Steve Mestrovitch staged a strong-man contest.
The young men were showing off. They came from all up and
down the Monongahela River to this picnic to compete in feats of
strength. They eyed the girls and felt strong.

Steve Mestrovitch was an open-hearth worker, and everybody
in the valley wanted to marry Steve's daughter Mary—for Mary
was a beauty. But Steve said Mary would marry the strongest man
in the world, no one else. Because Mary was tired of waiting, "being seventeen already," Steve decided to stage this contest. Mary

herself loved Peter Pussick and did not care about the strong-man contest.

All the men, women, and children from all the steel-mill towns on the river dressed up and came forth to the picnic. The strength test was to be lifting dolly bars. The little eighteen-inch dolly bars weighed 350 pounds each; the next size were 500-pounders; the big ones were double that.

The young men lined up. Whoever couldn't lift the little dolly bars was laughed at and had to go sit on the benches with the children. Whoever could not lift the 500-pounders had to go sit with the women. Whoever could lift the big one would get the girl!

So the boys pulled off their shirts and went to it. Only one or two were so weak they couldn't handle the little dollies. But only three boys made the grade on the second ones! And they nearly busted their eyes out trying to budge the big one. One of them pulled so hard that his hand came loose, but the big bar never left the ground.

Suddenly a big roar of a laugh was heard in the crowd.

"Who's that?" they yelled. "Let the laugher come pick up the bar."

A big man stepped out of the crowd and walked out on the field. His back was as big as a door, his neck like a bull's. He was seven feet tall. The prettiest man in the world, the girls all thought.

He picked up the big bar in one hand and shook it!

"Who are you?" said Steve.

"Joe Magarac."

Everybody laughed, because *magarac* in the Hungarian language means donkey or jackass.

"Magarac?"

"Sure. I work all the time. Look! I'm the only steel man in the world!"

He pulled off his shirt and, sure enough, he was all pure steel— hands, arms, legs, body, everything.

The people stared.

Joe Magarac just laughed and twisted the dolly bars in his two hands and let them stare. When Steve Mestrovitch saw this, he thought here was the husband for Mary. This was the strongest man in the world. But Joe said he had no time for home life; all he had time for was work. He was very polite about it. Mary was a fine wife for a marrying man, he said. But he, Joe Magarac, had time only for work. So Steve Mestrovitch gave up after this, and Mary got the young Peter Pussick she had set her heart on.

Joe wanted a job in the steel mill and got it. He got an open-hearth job on the No. 7 furnace, and he worked day and night. He only stopped to eat five meals a day, never for sleep or rest, and he never got tired. Some days when he didn't have time to go to the boardinghouse to eat, he drank hot steel soup.

Joe Magarac worked with his hands. He stirred the cooking steel with his hands and scooped it up by the handful and poured it into the ingot molds. He often made horseshoes and cannonballs with his bare hands. He'd grab the hot steel and squeeze out eight fine steel railroad rails at once from between his fingers, four to each hand.

Once just as a big ladle with fifty tons of boiling steel in it passed right over his crew, the chain broke. But Joe caught it just as it broke, and no one was hurt.

One day the smelter boss walked into the place and found Joe Magarac sitting in a ladle with the boiling steel bubbling up around his neck. This was his utmost gift to the work, he said: himself. He had heard they needed the finest steel in the world to build a new mill, so he was giving himself for that purpose. He was finer steel than the ore from the mountain, he said. And as things turned out, he was. Hungarian and Slovak steelworkers tell this story with tears in their eyes. They are very proud of Joe Magarac, and everybody still talks about him. There is a perpetual argument between the Slovak and Irish steelworkers, however, for the Irish declare his name was Joe McGarrick.

Gib Morgan

GIB MORGAN was an oil driller, hero and poet of the Pennsylvania oil fields. He was a tall old fellow with a wide gray mustache, always dressed in the typical blue flannel shirt, blue jeans, and high boots of the oil fields, with a dirty old derby on the side of his head. He had an old tomcat named Josiah who could lick any dog in Oil Center. Gib Morgan was a real person: Gilbert Morgan, born in Clarion County, Pennsylvania, died in 1909, an old veteran of the Union Army, tall-tale hero and tall-tale teller, and often the hero of his own tall tales. Gib made them up himself.

Wherever there is an oil derrick in this country there is the story of how Gib had to build a high roof over his big derrick to keep the oil from shooting a hole in the sky.

58

Once down in western Texas Gib drilled an oil well 3,000 feet into a sandy hill. A big wind came and blew all the sand away from around it, and next day, there was the hole, reaching 3,000 feet up in the air. Gib hated to *waste* it, so he set to work and cut it into four-foot lengths and sold them for postholes. That was the summer it was so dry there, Gib said, that the people had to fasten the stamps on their letters with safety pins.

Gib Morgan built the biggest pipeline in the country (the one from Philadelphia to New York) and admitted it. He pumped his partner through it one night because the man was in a hurry to get home and stop his wife's elopement. But the poor fellow got going so fast that he split in two at the Y where the line branches off in New Jersey. Gib always felt sorry about this because he had forgotten to warn him.

STATE LORE

Alabama

STATE FLOWER *goldenrod*

STATE BIRD *yellowhammer*

THE State of Alabama is named for the Alabamas, an Indian tribe whose name in their own language probably comes from *alba amo,* weed gatherer. They were so called because they used to gather the evergreen leaves of a kind of holly from which they made their famous "black drink," which gave them visions.

Nicknames: Cotton State, Lizard State, Yellowhammer State

Alabama is called the Cotton State for the obvious reason that cotton is the main crop. It is called the Yellowhammer State because one day a young Negro cattle driver from north-central Alabama didn't know the difference between a yellowhammer (a popular name for the flicker, or golden-winged woodpecker) and a parrot.

In the days before the Civil War, the people of north-central Alabama used to drive their cattle to Augusta, Georgia, to the big cattle market. One day a stalwart young Negro drover named

Sam, having properly delivered his herd, asked for some time off to see the city. Leave was granted, and he started out.

He walked slowly through the residential section, admiring the fine houses. In front of one mansion he saw a bright-colored parrot in a tree. The parrot also saw Sam and gave a great scream.

Sam said, "Hush that!"

The parrot cried, "Stop! Stop!" and let loose a stream of cuss words Sam had never heard before. Sam picked up a stick and threw it at the insolent bird. "Help," yelled the parrot. "Help! Help!"

Just then a houseboy ran out of the house to see what the rumpus was.

"Don't kill that valuable bird!" he cried to Sam.

"Valuable bird!" said Sam. "We got millions of those old yellowhammers in Alabama—but they got more manners!"

This story spread until everybody in Augusta, Georgia, was calling Alabama the Yellowhammer State.

Alabama is also known as the Lizard State, not only because lizards abound on the banks of its streams, but because the first settlers built their homes and little towns along the streams that wind through its woodlands. Their stream-side and river-bank type of life was likened to that of lizards. For this reason people from Alabama are sometimes called Lizards.

Arizona

STATE FLOWER *saguaro, or giant cactus*

STATE BIRD *cactus wren*

SOME people think that the name Arizona comes from the Spanish words: *árida,* meaning arid, dry, barren, and *zona,* region. But the most accepted explanation today is that it comes from the Papago Indian word *ari-sonac,* meaning little springs, or few springs.

Nicknames: Apache State, Baby State, Sunset State, Valentine State

Arizona is called the Apache State because the Apache Indians were the first inhabitants of the region. It is called the Sunset State because of its spectacular sunsets. It is called the Baby State because it was the last (48th) state to join the Union; and it is called the Valentine State because it was admitted to the Union on St. Valentine's Day, February 14, 1912.

The people of Arizona are called Sand Cutters because the wagon wheels of the first settlers cut the first trails in the sand.

There are all kinds of cracks and slams about Arizona weather. Arizona is the land where "it ain't rained since Noah," and the people who save for a rainy day never get a chance to spend their money. Arizona would be wonderful cattle country, they say, if it had any grass and water. It's so dry that there are frogs in Arizona seven years old that haven't learned to swim yet. And it's so hot that they have to ship in cracked ice from California for the chickens so the hens won't lay hard-boiled eggs. (Some people don't believe this.) But the air! Cars stop at gas stations all the way across the state just to fill their tires with soft, dry Arizona air.

Arizona boasts three of the wonders of nature: the Grand Canyon, the Painted Desert, and the Petrified Forest. The Grand Canyon, of course, is that big cut in the face of the earth, more than 200 miles long, dug by one of the Arizona old-timers. He will tell you about it himself. If you express a doubt, his pal will vouch for the truth of the matter; he knows, because *he* wheeled the dirt away.

The Painted Desert, with its vivid red and yellow rocks and sands, stretches for 200 miles from the Grand Canyon to the Petrified Forest, where hundreds of pine and cedar tree trunks stand petrified to red and yellow chalcedony. The story is that the petrified trees have petrified birds in the branches singing their petrified songs. You can see the little petrified bird-notes hanging in the air just as they were first sung, they say. And whoever doubts that one, asking why they don't fall to the ground, is told that here the force of gravitation is also petrified.

In Arizona, an old-timer, someone who remembers the days of the stagecoach and the overland 16-mule-team wagons, is called a Hassayamper. The name is derived from the Hassayampa River, which rises from the clear mountain springs in Yavapai County and flows slowly southward through the desert to the Gila River. Whoever drinks of Hassayampa water, upstream or downstream, is forever after gifted with the tall-tale tongue. "Lying waters," some people say, but that is hardly true, for every Hassayamper believes

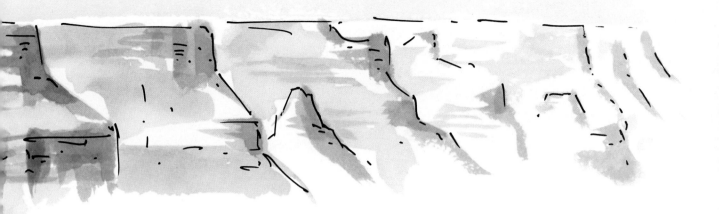

his own tales. The Hassayamper will never be poor, and he'll never be rich, and he doesn't care. He'll never leave Arizona, or if he does, he'll always come back. Even a greenhorn Easterner, they say, once he has drunk from the Hassayampa, becomes a Hassayamper and can tell as tall a tale as any old-timer.

Arkansas

STATE FLOWER *apple blossom*

STATE BIRD *mockingbird*

THE State of Arkansas was named for a tribe of Sioux Indians who in their own language were called the *Quapaw,* or "downstream people," because they separated from a larger group and moved downstream to settle at the mouth of a river. But the name Quapaw was seldom given them by outsiders. The Illinois Indians called them *Akansa* or *Arkansas,* and so did the various white explorers who heard about them. And Arkansas was the name given to the state and to the river at whose mouth they lived.

Nicknames: Bear State, Bowie State, Toothpick State, Wonder State

Arkansas was called the Bear State because it used to be full of

67

bears. It was called the Bowie State because Arkansans claim that the original bowie knife was made in Arkansas for cutting up bear meat, and that no true bowie knife was ever made anywhere else. Everybody in the state had one—man, woman, and child. "Arkansas toothpicks," they were called, for outsiders said the people used their ten-inch bowie knives for everything, even toothpicks! And the people themselves were called Toothpicks for this reason. The official nickname of Arkansas, however, is the Wonder State, adopted in 1923, just because it is full of wonders, especially mineral wonders, including the only diamond mine in the United States.

The Arkansas Traveler is a story, a fiddle tune, a hoedown, a magazine, two paintings, a vaudeville skit, a patchwork-quilt pattern, and a person; it is probably one of the most famous bits of folklore in all North America.

Colonel Sandford C. Faulkner (1803–1874) was the weary horseback traveler through Arkansas who got lost in the mountains in the fall of 1840. He was tired, hungry, thirsty, and so was his horse; night was coming on, and no town was in sight. At last he came upon a squatter's cabin. The squatter was sitting in front of it playing on a fiddle—the same tune over and over.

"Hello, stranger."

"Hello, yourself."

"Can I get something to eat here?"

"Ain't got a thing in the house."

"Can I get a drink?"

"Drank the last drop this morning."

"Can't you give my horse something?"

"Ain't got nuthin for him."

"Well, how far is it to the next house?"

"Dunno. Never been thar."

"Well, who lives here?"

"I do."

"And what might your name be?"

"Might be Tom, might be Harry, but it ain't neither one."

"Will you tell me where this road goes?"

"Never gone anywhere; stays right there."

"Since I cannot reach another house tonight, may I sleep here? I'll tie my horse to the tree. Never mind about food or drink."

"House leaks. Only one dry spot in it, and me and Sal sleeps on that. Can't tie the horse to that tree, neither, because Sal don't want the persimmons shook off of it."

"Why don't you mend the roof where it leaks?"

"Been raining all day."

"You could mend it on a fine day."

"It don't leak on a fine day."

All this time the squatter was still playing the same tune over and over.

"Why don't you finish that tune?"

"Can't get the turn of the tune."

So the traveler took the fiddle and played the turn of the tune and finished it off. It went like this:

"Stranger, take half a dozen chairs and set down! Sal, cut a hunk off that buck I killed and cook it! Get out the black jug and give us some whisky! Chase the dog outa the bread tray! Untie the knot in the rag and give us some sugar! Tom, take that hoss to the shed and give him fodder and corn. Play away, stranger. You kin sleep on the dry spot tonight."

Arkansas mosquitoes are worth mention. Hunters and river fishermen talk about catching them in traps and fighting them off with paddles and shotguns. A man brought one home one day, thinking to break it in to mule harness and use it for plowing and other farm work. But it snapped the harness and flew off with one of the man's cows. This story is probably an exaggeration. Truthful Arkansans admit it would take two to make off with a cow.

The mosquitoes of Crawford County, Arkansas, are a special breed and can be identified by a white spot two inches wide between the eyes.

California

STATE FLOWER *California, or golden, poppy*

STATE BIRD *California quail*

ONE man's guess is as good as another's about how California got its name. Since it was discovered by Spanish explorers it does not seem unreasonable that the word California might come from two Spanish words, *caliente fornelo,* hot furnace, an accurate enough description of the climate in the southern part.

The favorite story, however, is that the old Spanish explorers were familiar with a romance, *Las Sergas de Esplandión,* published in 1510, which described an island "beyond the Indies" named California, and when they came upon the peninsula which is now Lower California, thought they had come to it. In 1533 Fortuno Ximenes discovered this "island" west of Mexico. Two years later Hernando Cortés landed at the same spot, thought it was an island, and named it California.

Some people say that the name comes from two words of a Lower

70

California Indian language, *kali forno,* meaning high hills. There are four or five other equally unconvincing explanations, but nobody knows for sure.

Nicknames: El Dorado State, Golden State

Both nicknames are given to California because of the discovery of gold there in 1848 and the famous, romantic, and spectacular gold rush of 1849. Californians are still called Gold Diggers from those adventurous days. The people who poured into California in search of gold were called Rushers, or Forty-Niners, or Argonauts from the old Greek legend of the men who sailed to Colchis in search of the Golden Fleece.

California is the land of brag. It has the brightest sunshine, the healthiest climate, the richest soil, the biggest vegetables, and the highest rents of any state. Any California child who knows his local history can tell you that the climate is so healthy that they had to shoot a man (a stranger, of course) in order to start the first graveyard in his town. Of course, everybody wants to live in California, and the new towns pop up so fast that the trains keep a man on the rear platform to write down the ones that spring up after the train goes by. They used to try to stop at them all on the way back, but had to give that up.

Everybody's grandfather lived to be 200 years old—in perfect health. The old man got bored and tired of living, but just couldn't sicken or die. Finally a friend suggested that he make his will and then travel and see the rest of the world. So this he did, and sure enough, not long after he left California he took sick and died—just as he had wished.

His will requested his heir to bury him in his native soil. So his body was brought back and the funeral service solemnly held. Everyone rejoiced that the old man had his wish at last. But the wonderful health-giving, life-giving air of California revived him, and he rose up, sprier than ever. His heir was somewhat distressed about this and kindly suggested more travel, but the old man himself thought, oh, well, he might as well stick it out till his time came.

Colorado

STATE FLOWER *columbine (white and purple)*

STATE BIRD *lark bunting*

THE State of Colorado is named for its river, which was so dubbed by the Spanish explorers because of its muddy waters colored by the reddish land through which it flows. The word *colorado* is from the Spanish *colorar,* to color.

Nicknames: Buffalo Plains State, Centennial State, Lead State, Silver State

You hardly ever hear Colorado called the Buffalo Plains State any more—not since the white man killed off all the buffalo. Centennial State is the official nickname because Colorado joined the Union in 1876, exactly one hundred years after the Declaration of Independence was signed. It is called the Lead State and the Silver State because of its extensive lead and silver mining, and the people are called Silverines because so many of them made their fortunes from the silver mines. The old nickname of Rovers still sticks to them, too, from the gold-fever days in 1858 when the settlers couldn't stay settled but went a-roving to Pikes Peak by the hundreds, seeking gold.

Colorado is the highest state in the Union. It has 1,500 mountain peaks over 10,000 feet high, and fifty-one more than 14,000 feet high. It is the state of breath-taking scenery, the state of high mountains and high winds, where all three dimensions can be measured in miles, and the people have to feed the chickens buckshot to keep them from blowing away. Colorado is the country that the big Stetson cowboy hat was made for—the hat that will keep off rain, snow, hail, or sun, and keep out cold or heat—the hat that will hold enough oats or corn to feed a horse and won't leak if man or beast needs water. It is the land where the cowboys sing

to the cattle when riding herd at night. And it's the land of the slide-rock bolter which feeds on tourists.

The slide-rock bolter is a big-headed, slit-eyed animal with a mouth that runs in a straight line all round its face to behind the ears. It has a forked tail equipped with grab hooks, by which it holds to a mountain peak or ridge, and just lies there, watching the gulches for tourists. When it sees one, or a party of tourists, it lets go and slides with toboggan speed down the mountain, open-mouthed, scoops in the tourists without stopping, and zooms up the next mountain to the top. Here the tail grabs onto the peak again, and the slide-rock bolter hangs at rest, waiting for the next tourist. About the only way to catch one is to rig up a dummy in a sport coat with a Colorado guidebook in its hand and stuff it with strychnine or explosives. Quite a number were caught this way, but slide-rock bolters are so keen-eyed that soon they were scooping up the trap setters and leaving the dummies alone. Now some guides won't take tourists very far into the hills.

Connecticut

STATE FLOWER *mountain laurel*

STATE BIRD *American robin*

THE State of Connecticut is named for its river, which the Algonquian Indians of that region called *quinnehtukgut,* meaning long river, before the white man ever saw it.

Nicknames: Nutmeg State, Blue Law State, Constitution State, Land of Steady Habits

"Here's to the Nutmeg State! Where is a grater?" This 100-year-old toast bears witness to the pride Connecticut takes in its nickname. It is called the Nutmeg State because it was the home of the original Yankee peddler who could sell anybody anything—even wooden nutmegs. The Connecticut peddler traveled all over the country in his horse and buggy, with his buttons and needles and pins, kitchen gadgets and clocks. "Any wooden nutmegs? Any calico hog troughs today, lady?" is said to have been one of his traditional greetings. And his reputation for shrewdness and slick tricks (symbolized by the wooden nutmeg) made Connecticut famous everywhere. The people are still called Nutmegs.

Connecticut is called the Blue Law State because of its severe laws in the seventeenth century against breaking the Sabbath in any way, against cursing, against drunkenness or even drinking hard liquor, against the use of tobacco, against family quarrels or lack of family discipline, any fanciness of dress, and even against keeping Christmas and making mince pies, playing musical instruments, or other innocent amusements. Along with this too goes the nickname of the Land of Steady Habits.

It is called the Constitution State because its famous document, the Fundamental Orders of 1639, was the first constitution written by the people themselves in this country.

No story about Connecticut would be complete without a Yankee peddler story. One night a Connecticut peddler traveling through southern Virginia stopped at a tavern and asked to spend the night. There was great prejudice against Yankee peddlers in that section, and for a time the innkeeper refused. At last he consented. "But," he said, "only if you will play us a Yankee trick before you go." The peddler said he would be glad to do this and, being tired, went to bed.

In the morning he carefully folded up the coverlet on the bed and put it in his case. He went downstairs to breakfast and, while eating, he opened the case and urged the landlady to buy some of his wares. She was greatly taken with the coverlet. It exactly matched one of hers, she said, and the low price the peddler put on it soon turned the deal.

The peddler counted his money, got into his buggy, and drove off. But before he was out of earshot the innkeeper called after him. "I didn't see any Yankee trick!"

"You will," said the peddler, and drove on.

Delaware

STATE FLOWER   *peach blossom*

STATE BIRD   *blue hen's chicken*

THE State of Delaware was named for the Delaware River, which was named for Delaware Bay, which was named for Thomas West, Lord Delaware (or De La Warr), the first governor of Virginia. It was so named in 1610 by Captain Samuel Argall, who was taking a ship from England to Virginia. The ship had been so battered and beset by storms en route that the first haven he came to, the quiet bay at the mouth of the Delaware River, he named, in gratitude for delivery from storm and sea, after the governor of the land which was his destination.

77

Nicknames: Blue Hen State, or Blue Hen's Chicken's State; Diamond State; First State; Uncle Sam's Pocket Handkerchief

Delaware is called the Blue Hen State after the ancestress of two famous fighting cocks which went to the wars with their owner during the American Revolution. They belonged to young Captain Caldwell of Delaware, who said they were the chickens of a certain old blue hen at home. They were famous fighters and when pitted against each other fought with such fury that onlooking soldiers used to yell: "We're sons of the old Blue Hen!" or "We're the Blue Hen's chickens, we are!" or "We're the Blue Hen's chickens! We're game to the end!" Thus from their love of cock-fighting the Delaware regiments were called the Blue Hen's Chickens, and their state became known as the Blue Hen State. People from Delaware are still called the Blue Hen's Chickens.

Delaware is called the First State because it was the first to sign the Constitution of the United States.

It is called the Diamond State because its importance is greater than its size. And the epithet Uncle Sam's Pocket Handkerchief refers to its smallness, too. There are all kinds of cracks and slams about the size of Delaware. There are only three counties in the whole state, and one old saw adds ". . . and only two at high tide." The people are sometimes called Muskrats because, the joke is, only muskrats could keep a toe hold in so small a place.

Florida

STATE FLOWER *orange blossom*

STATE BIRD *mockingbird*

FLORIDA was named by Juan Ponce de León in 1513 for the sight that met his eyes as he approached the land: *Tierra Florida,* Land of Flowers, for the masses of wild flowers in bloom as far as he could see. Or he may have named it for the day he first put foot on land, the day of the Feast of Flowers, *Pascua Florida* (Easter). It does not matter which; it could have been both.

Nicknames: Alligator State; Everglade State; Flower State, or Land of Flowers; Orange State; Peninsula State

Florida is called the Alligator State because its creeks and rivers and swamps are full of alligators. Hundreds of baby alligators are sold to tourists every year. And the people are called Alligators, because the census takers report the population to be about half and half.

It is called the Everglade State because most of the state is everglade land—low, swampy land covered with tall saw grass and water prairies dotted with hammocks of thick vegetation. The whole everglade section is itself called the Everglades, home and

refuge of the rare egret, the great heron, and other water birds.

Florida is called the Flower State because of the abundance of flowers for which it was named. And it is called the Orange State because of its many orange groves. Its nickname Peninsula State comes from the fact that almost the whole state is a peninsula.

Besides being called Alligators the people are sometimes called Fly-up-the-creeks after the shy little green heron that haunts its streams.

Florida brags about its sunshine and its hurricanes. A favorite sunshine story is the one about the young man dying of tuberculosis who was put on the train for Florida. He was accompanied by a nurse and given constant care in the hope that if he could survive the trip, Florida sun would prolong his life. As the train slowed up for one of the first stops across the Florida state line, the passenger in the next seat pushed up his window blind, and the wonderful Florida sun poured in on the invalid. He rose up and rapidly left the train at the next station. Everyone was astounded, but when they rushed out after him, he had disappeared. A search was made, and a few days later the young man was found. He had joined up with the circus in its winter quarters and had a job as a lion tamer.

The east coast of Florida is headquarters for hurricanes, and the reason is that it belongs to the Devil. And the way the Devil got it is a Christmas story.

All over the South it is a Christmas custom for the people to say "Christmas gift!" to each other, and if somebody says this first, the one thus greeted has to give him a present. Well, once when God was walking around in Florida on a Christmas Day, the Devil thought he would like to have God give him a present. So he hid behind a stump, and when God came along he jumped out and yelled, "Christmas gift!"

God was tricked for sure, so he said, "You can have the east coast," and walked on. And now the Devil does have fun playing hurricanes up and down it.

Georgia

STATE FLOWER *Cherokee rose*

STATE BIRD *brown thrasher*

GEORGIA was named for King George II of England in 1732, when General James Edward Oglethorpe and his nineteen associates received the charter from that king appointing them trustees to administer the colony.

Nicknames: Buzzard State, Cracker State, Goober State, Peach State

Georgia is called the Buzzard State because of its time-honored laws protecting buzzards as valuable scavengers. It is called the Cracker State for its numerous impoverished white citizens in the rural sections, who are called crackers. It is traditional that Oglethorpe wanted the colony to be a refuge for Englishmen hopelessly incarcerated in debtors' prisons, and many of these had their way paid to Georgia by the trustees of the colony. "To crack," in seventeenth- and eighteenth-century English slang, meant to break out of jail, and the breakers-out were called "crackers." From the early sixteenth century, "cracked" meant bankrupt, ruined, penniless, and in America, gradually took on the meaning of ignorant, low-class, also.

Georgia is called the Goober State because of its big annual crop of peanuts, or goobers. The word goober comes from the Bantu Negro word, *nguba,* meaning peanut. Georgians themselves are sometimes called Goober-grabbers. It is called the Peach State because it produces more peaches than any other state in the East.

Georgia is the land where any preacher can drive up to a house door and be sure of sitting down to a good chicken dinner. This is why all the barnyard fowl run for the woods the minute they see a preacher coming. "Going to *cut, cut, cut* your head off," the hens yell in a panic as they run.

81

The crows are in the corn is an old Georgia saying for "time to get up," or "it is getting late." It originates in a Negro folk tale told all over the South, especially to children who are sleepyheads, but it is usually told as having "happened in Georgia." It was told to me as a child by a South Carolina grandmother as having happened in Georgia "not long ago."

The people in the house didn't wake up very early one Sunday morning, but slept and slept and slept. The crows didn't see anybody stirring, so they all gathered down in the cornfield and began to pull up and eat the young shoots of corn.

"Ca–awn! Ca–awn! Ca–awn!" they exclaimed.

The old yard rooster saw this happening and yelled, "Get–up–get–up! The crows are in the ca–a–wn!"

But the people didn't hear him. They went right on sleeping, and the crows went right on eating the corn. "Ca–awn! Ca–awn! Ca–awn!"

The old rooster got more and more worried. In a loud voice he crowed, "The crows a–pulling up the ca–a–awn!" But the people went right on sleeping, and the crows kept right on eating the corn.

So the old rooster gave up—no use to crow anymore. Finally the

old turkey gobbler in the yard commented on the situation. "Lord–a–mighty! Cawn all–et–up–all–et–up–all–et–up." And when the people finally woke up that day they found the corn all et up.

A friend of mine from Georgia says that when she was a little girl her mother used to stand at the foot of the stairs to call her to get up for school, imitating the crow of a rooster with the words "The crows are in the ca–a–awn!"

Idaho

STATE FLOWER   *syringa,* or *mock orange*

STATE BIRD   *mountain bluebird*

IDAHO was officially named in 1863 when it was made a Territory by Act of Congress. But the name was not suddenly pulled out of a hat for the occasion. It was already an old name on the lips of miners seeking gold along the Clearwater, Salmon, and Boise rivers in 1860, '61, and '62. *Idaho* is a Shoshone Indian word, *ee-da-how* (*ee,* coming down; *da,* sun, and also mountain; *how,* an exclamation), which the white man took to mean "It's daybreak." Literally it means "Behold! The sun coming down the mountain," and anyone who has ever seen the sun come up from behind a mountain knows exactly how the light "comes down" the hither side.

Nicknames: Gem State, or Gem of the Mountains; Little Ida

Idaho is called the Gem of the Mountains because historians like to think that the Indians saw the sun as a gem when it blazed up from behind a peak. It is called Little Ida because it is the smallest of the Western states. The people are called Fortune-seekers because of the hordes of settlers who came into the region seeking gold when gold was discovered at Orofino in 1860.

Idaho is the land of vast forests and big potatoes. Even New Yorkers eat Idaho potatoes. Ask any Idahoan what makes the potatoes so big, and he will explain that they are fertilized with corn meal and watered with milk (not watered milk). Any night you can go out into the field and put your ear to the ground and hear the potatoes grumbling at each other to "lay over and stop crowding." An Idaho farmer who had potatoes for sale was asked by a camper one time if he would sell him a hundred pounds. "Can't do it," was the answer. "I wouldn't cut into a potato for *any*one!"

Illinois

STATE FLOWER *violet*

STATE BIRD *cardinal*

THE State of Illinois takes its name from the Illinois River, which the French explorer Robert Cavelier de La Salle named in 1679 for a group of Indians whom he found living along its banks. These people called themselves *iliniwek,* meaning men or people, and Illinois is the way La Salle and his French companions said it.

Nicknames: Corn State, Egypt, Prairie State, Sucker State

Illinois is called the Corn State because it is one of the greatest corn-raising states in the Union. It is called Egypt (southern Illinois especially is called Egypt) because of its frequent floods and consequent fertility and perhaps also because of Cairo, the southernmost town in the state. Local legend has it that one year during a long, bad drought in northern Illinois the farmers flocked into the southern part to buy wheat and oats and corn. And this pilgrimage was likened to the ancient pilgrimage of the Israelites into Egypt seeking corn after drought.

The official nickname of Illinois is the Prairie State because the greater part of it is wide, green, unbroken prairie. It is sometimes called the Sucker State because thirsty riders over the wide, hot prairies in summer used to refresh themselves by drinking out of the crawfish holes which were plentiful. In the bottom of every crawfish hole there is cool, pure fresh water, which people drank by sucking the water up through long hollow reeds which grew near-by.

One of the stories Illinoisans love to tell is about the man from Sangamon County who found himself standing before the gates of heaven. He knocked. St. Peter poked his head out and asked where he was from.

"Sangamon County, Illinois."

"Go back," said St. Peter. "There is nothing here as beautiful as Sangamon County."

Indiana

STATE FLOWER *zinnia*

STATE BIRD *cardinal*

INDIANA is the Indian land that was ceded to the Philadelphia Trading Company by the Six Nations of the Iroquois Confederacy in 1768. The word is a New Latin word coined to mean "the land of the Indians."

Nickname: Hoosier State

There are several stories explaining why Indianans are called Hoosiers. One story says they got the name from their insatiable curiosity; they were always looking around or poking their heads in doors and saying, "Who's here?" Another story says that in pioneer times the men of Indiana were so big and strong that they never failed to hush any opponent—sometimes permanently! The bully of every town was called a "husher," and their French Louisiana neighbors pronounced the word "hoosher." Hoosiers themselves prefer this last story.

Indiana is the state where the liars' bench is not just a phrase on somebody's tongue, but a real bench under a locust tree in front of the courthouse in Nashville, Brown County. It holds six, and here Indiana tall-talers gather to swap their whoppers. When the bench is full, the sixth man gets shoved off (at the end of the bench that has no arm), and the newcomer sits down at the head of the row. There is never an empty seat.

Iowa

STATE FLOWER *wild rose*

STATE BIRD *goldfinch*

THE State of Iowa takes its name from a tribe of Sioux Indians who originally occupied the region and whom the Dakota Indians called *Ayuhwa,* or sleepy ones. Early French and Spanish explorers also called these people *Ayuhwa* and spelled the name *Ayoua, Aioua, Ajoues,* with other variations. The English, when they came, spelled it Ioway, and Iowans themselves still pronounce their state I″o-way′. Finally the spelling Iowa was formally adopted for the state.

Nickname: Hawkeye State

The nickname Hawkeye State is said to come from an Indian chief named Hawkeye, who, with his bands, harassed early travelers through that territory. The people are also called Hawkeyes.

Some people say that the letters *i-o-w-a* spell corn, and the letters *c-o-r-n* spell hogs, for Iowa is famous as the corn and hog state. But Iowa is also the state that has 114 folk cures for warts (one of them is to rub your wart when you see a stranger and say, "Take it, stranger") and the state where a penny will keep the Devil out of your pocketbook. Old-timers say they learned their multiplication tables in school to the tune of "Yankee Doodle." Sing this:

Five times seven is thirty-five,
And five times eight is forty.
Five times nine is forty-five,
And five times ten is fifty.

87

Kansas

STATE FLOWER *sunflower*

STATE BIRD *western meadowlark*

THE State of Kansas is named for the Kansas River, which takes its name from a tribe of Sioux Indians, the Kansa, who lived along its banks, and whose name means South-wind People.

Nicknames: Cyclone State, Grasshopper State, Jayhawker State, Squatter State, Sunflower State

Kansas is called the Cyclone State because it is the very cyclone center of the United States.

It is called the Grasshopper State from the terrible years 1874–1876 when Rocky Mountain grasshoppers descended on Kansas and neighboring states and devoured everything before them, and the people all but starved. Some of them did. The grasshoppers ate the corn and wheat, the gardens and fruits, leaving the ground bare and the trees stripped. They ate the starched lace curtains in the people's houses; they ate everything they could find in household pantries and went into the barns and milksheds and drank the milk. Women were even afraid to take the lids off boiling kettles, lest the creatures leap into them and the family be forced to eat grasshopper stew.

The term "Kansas grit" may have originated during this plague, for in this time of fear and starvation, when the ground was covered with grasshoppers and people shook them out of their sleeves, one of the Kansas papers dryly commented in a short news item, "A grasshopper was seen on the courthouse steps at 8:30 this morning."

Kansas has been called the Jayhawker State since the days of the Kansas-Missouri border troubles in 1856 (and during the Civil

War) when "jayhawker" meant a bush fighter, pillager, guerrilla. The word originally meant "a natural-born thief not averse to murder," and was applied to the pillagers and guerrillas on both sides of the border. Kansans took it proudly to themselves, however, and the name has stuck ever since. In modern Kansas folklore the jayhawk is a big bird with yellow feet and big goggle eyes who always flies backward. He doesn't care where he's going "but he sure wants to know where he's been."

Kansas is called the Squatter State in memory of the hordes of squatters who poured in and settled on the land about 1854.

Sunflower State is the official nickname of Kansas, chosen for the big wild sunflowers that grow so profusely in the fields and along the roadsides.

Talk about Jack and the beanstalk! That story can't hold a candle to the story of Jack and the Kansas corn, except that there are no giants in it—no giants but the corn itself, that is.

One day a Kansas farmer sent his son Jack to look over the cornfield. Jack wasn't tall enough to look over the cornfield, so he took along a ladder. He leaned it up against one of the cornstalks and started to climb. He climbed up the ladder and on up to the top of the cornstalk and saw such a wonder of golden corn for miles around that he could hardly wait to tell his father of the rich harvest they were going to have.

But when he started to come down he realized that the corn had gone on growing all the time he was up there. And as he stepped down from joint to joint, the corn kept right on growing up—faster than he could get down. He couldn't get to the bottom no matter how hard he tried or how fast he stepped.

After a while the farmer began to wonder why Jack was so long coming back. No use to go hunting him through the forest of corn. Anyone would have sense enough to see that. So the farmer climbed to the top of his windmill and soon spied Jack in the top of a cornstalk across the field, frantically waving his red bandanna.

The farmer called his neighbors together for help, and soon five big men with axes were chopping away at the cornstalk, trying to rescue Jack. But the cornstalk kept growing, and the axes never hit into the same notch twice. It kept right on growing with notch after notch cut into it about eighteen inches apart. Night came, and the men were still chopping, and Jack was still up there.

This went on for days—the men chopping, the corn growing, and Jack still up there. All he had to eat was raw corn, and he got awful tired of that, but no help for it. Raw corn or starve.

After a while the drought came, and the corn stopped growing. Jack was finally able to climb down. He certainly was glad. He was a smart, enterprising boy; he gathered up the heap of corncobs he had thrown down and made them into corncob pipes and sold them to tourists.

Kentucky

STATE FLOWER   *goldenrod*

STATE BIRD   *cardinal*

HOW Kentucky got its name and what the name means is still a controversy. It is said that a Colonel Richard Henderson bought a piece of land from the Cherokee Indians in 1774 which was called *Canetuckee.* And the old historians spelled it variously: Cantucky, Kentuckee, Kaintuck. Some writers report that this is a Cherokee word, meaning prairie; others say it is from an Iroquois Indian word *kentake,* meaning meadow or pasture land. A familiar and popular explanation is that the word *kentuke* means bloody river, or bloody ground, and refers to old enmities and wars between the Cherokee and the Iroquois Indians.

Nicknames: Bluegrass State, Corn-cracker State, Dark and Bloody Ground

Kentucky is called the Bluegrass State because of its great, rich, rolling bluegrass country in the very heart of the state, the land of Kentucky whisky and Kentucky horses. It is called the Corn-cracker State in reference to the unmoneyed mountain-white population in the eastern mountains. It is called Dark and Bloody Ground in memory of those old Indian wars mentioned above.

The people themselves are called Bears, because in pioneer times the population of Kentucky numbered more bears than folks. The Corn-crackers are the Kentucky mountain-whites.

All Kentucky is divided into three parts: the eastern mountains, the bluegrass region, and the river country to the west. It is the land of mint juleps and Southern colonels and race horses and moonshine and mountain-white blood feuds. Kentucky is proud of its log-cabin tradition, proud of being the land where log-cabin boys studied by firelight and became famous men, where "the people learned to do the best they could with what they got."

Kentucky is still the romantic backwoods state where a man prides himself on being a crack shot with a rifle. He can drive a nail at a hundred yards. In Kentucky "to drive a nail" means just that, and "to snuff the candle" means to put a shot through the flame of a lighted candle without putting it out.

The Kentucky backwoodsman has been known as the half-man, half-horse, half-alligator hero for nearly 200 years: the kind of man who can beat his weight in wildcats, "wade the Mississippi, leap the Ohio"; he brags that he has "a touch of the snapping turtle" in him, or "a touch of the steamboat," and he will roar to prove it; in fact, "ring-tailed roarer" is one of his proudest epithets.

Louisiana

STATE FLOWER *magnolia*

STATE BIRD *brown pelican*

LOUISIANA was named by the French explorer La Salle in 1682 in honor of the king of France, then Louis XIV.

Nicknames: Child of the Mississippi, Creole State, Pelican State, Sugar State

Louisiana is called the Child of the Mississippi because this river dominates the life of the state, and much of its southern area was formed through countless ages from the silt deposited by that great river. It is called the Creole State because some of its citizens are Creoles, descendants of the original French and Spanish settlers. It is called the Pelican State because pelicans are numerous along its streams, bayous, and shores. The state coat of arms shows a pelican. And it is called the Sugar State because of its many sugar plantations and refineries. The people are nicknamed either Creoles or Pelicans.

Louisiana is a land of bayous and pelicans, whose people reflect many cultures: of proud Creoles in the cities, who jealously guard their ancient traditions; of Cajuns, the descendants of some 7,000 Nova Scotia French *deportés* (Acadians) who began to pour into Louisiana in 1755, and among whom to be a neighbor is to be as close, loyal, loving, and beloved as blood kin; and of Negroes, the descendants of thousands of imported slaves (the first 500 were brought to Louisiana in 1716) who now outnumber the whites five to one in the plantation sections, and whose music, religion, and folklore help make Louisiana what it is. A Protestant white population occupies the northern part of the state.

The annual rowdy super carnival of New Orleans—Mardi Gras, or Fat Tuesday—which marks the last day before Lent, is famous

93

all over the world. On the night of Mardi Gras a certain restaurant in Royal Street still serves a delicious, expensive "ghost dinner" to an empty table for two, in memory of two young lovers who ate there on Mardi Gras, the eve of their troth, many years ago.

Louisiana seems to be inhabited by as many ghosts as mortals. Old plantation ghost bells can still be heard across the fields; every country road and old plantation house has its own special haunt; headless men walk or ride the backroads and mislead motorists whom they think have no business there. Ghosts of Negroes haunt their lynching trees. And there are ghosts of pirates all along the 1,000-mile Louisiana shore. The ghost of Jean Laffite is one of them.

People are still searching for Laffite's buried gold along the Gulf Coast. But treasure-digging is not undertaken without fortitude, for in addition to the back-breaking task itself, there are many digging taboos. Every Louisiana treasure hunter knows that you mustn't talk, spit, curse, or sweat while digging for treasure. If you do, you will never find it.

Louisiana also has its ghost river boat. The ghost of an old paddle wheeler chugs up and down Raccourci Cut-Off on foggy nights, trying to get out. The story is that the paddle wheeler was trapped in the cutoff one night when the Mississippi River changed its course. The pilot could find no way out, and he yelled and cursed and said he'd get out of there that night or he'd never get out! This kind of remark, of course, is just what calls up the Devil. The pilot never did get out. People can still hear the old engines chugging, the signal bell jangling, and the pilot cursing.

To drink from Bayou Teche is a proverbial phrase in southern Louisiana. To drink from Bayou Teche means that you will return to that water no matter how far you wander or how old you get. Bayou Teche is in Iberia Parish in southern Louisiana. The bayou got its name, so they say, from an Atakapas Indian word *tenche*, meaning snake. The story is that one day the Indians came upon a monstrous writhing snake and, after a struggle, overcame it. The serpentine bayou is that snake—Bayou Tenche, now Bayou Teche.

The folk beliefs of Louisiana include many of the same folk beliefs as the rest of the South and of the United States. A dog howling under the window foretells a death in the family, for instance, in Louisiana as elsewhere throughout America and Europe. "When the cat washes its face, company is coming" is a popular saying everywhere from Nova Scotia to Louisiana. A horse chestnut (or a potato) carried in the pocket cures rheumatism in Louisiana as surely as it does in Massachusetts. But rubbing the sore spot with rattlesnake oil or alligator fat is added to the list of rheumatism cures in Louisiana. In Louisiana it is impossible to kill a graveyard rabbit, and all old maids eventually turn into screech owls.

Maine

STATE FLOWER *pine cone and tassel*

STATE BIRD *chickadee*

THE generally accepted explanation of how the State of Maine received its name is that it was so called by the French for their own province of Main (Mayne, Meyne) in France. And the territory "of the maine land . . . lying upon the Sea Coast betwixt the rivers of Merimack and Sagadahoch and to the heads of these rivers" was named Province of Maine in 1622 by the

Council of New England in its charter. New England fishermen always interpreted the name to mean the main, or mainland, to distinguish it from the thousands of big and little islands which lie off its coast.

Nicknames: Border State, Lumber State, Old Dirigo State, Pine Tree State, Pole Star State

Maine is called the Border State because it borders on Canada. And it is called the Lumber State because its pine forests furnish a big percentage of the lumber used in the United States. The name Old Dirigo State comes from its motto, *Dirigo,* I direct, or guide. The official nickname is the Pine Tree State in honor of its vast pine forests—seventeen million acres of them. It is called the Pole

Star State not only because it is the northernmost of all the states but because the pole star guides its seafaring men safe home.

The people are called Down Easters, Foxes, Lumberjacks, and Pine Trees. The term Down Easters was given to Maine people in the old days by people around Boston when Maine was still a part of Massachusetts—stretching to the north and eastward. And they were called Foxes because foxes were formerly so abundant in the region. Maine people are called Lumberjacks, obviously, because so many of them are exactly that. They are called Pine Trees for their own state symbol, the tall, straight pine.

Maine is the state that looks like a Christmas card all winter. It is inhabited by fishermen, lobstermen, lumbermen, and 150,000 deer, and still enforces the ancient law that every schoolteacher has to teach children kindness to animals for ten minutes every day.

Fishermen of the Maine islands say the seagulls are their guardian spirits. The seagulls show them where to find the fish, for gulls fish for a living too, and wherever gulls gather, the fishermen know there are schools of fish. In thick fogs the crying of the gulls warns fishermen off the ledges. For these two reasons seagulls are protected by law in the State of Maine.

Maine is famous for its thick fogs that come in off the Bay of Fundy, "thick enough to drive a nail into," they say. Those thick Fundy fogs give rise to the story about a fisherman who took advantage of a foggy day to stay home and shingle his roof. He went up on the roof and started shingling right after breakfast and didn't come down till dinner time.

"Maggie, we got an almighty long house," he said to his wife.
So Maggie came out to look.

"Land sakes!" she said. "If you haven't shingled right out onto the fog!"

This story is especially associated with the coast of Maine, and it is told as having happened "right here" all the way from Kittery to Eastport. But it is a fog story and is told wherever there are fogs, especially Fundy fogs—from Cape Cod and Nantucket into New Brunswick, Nova Scotia, and Newfoundland.

Maryland

STATE FLOWER   *black-eyed Susan*

STATE BIRD   *Baltimore oriole*

WHEN George Calvert, Lord Baltimore, drew up the charter for the colony which is now the State of Maryland and handed it to King Charles I to sign, the king said, "And what shall be the name of this province?" Lord Baltimore answered that he had intended to name it for His Majesty, but that there was already a colony in the New World named Carolina. "Then let's name it for the Queen," said Charles. And so the name was written in: *Terra Mariae,* the Land of Maria. Thus Maryland was named for Henrietta Maria, the queen of Charles I of England, whom the people called Mary.

Nicknames: Cockade State, Old Line State, Oyster State, Queen State

Maryland is called the Cockade State because the young men in the Maryland Revolutionary troops were distinguished by their brilliant-colored cockades. There are two explanations for the nickname Old Line State. One is that Maryland was on the line which demarked the land grants of William Penn and the holdings of Lord Baltimore. Another is that during the Revolution Maryland was the only state that contributed regular troops to the line, and the Maryland Line was counted among the finest in the whole Continental army.

Maryland is called the Oyster State because of her extensive oyster fisheries, and Maryland oystermen say if you want lots of oysters—*sing.* This is why Maryland oystermen are said always to sing at their work.

It is called the Queen State because it was named for a queen.

The people of Maryland are called Claw-thumpers (sometimes Craw-thumpers) or Oysters. Claw-thumper is the lobsterman's nickname for lobsters, probably because of the thumping noise their big claws make as they scrabble frantically around in a boat or a box, and later the people themselves were called Claw-thumpers. They are often dubbed Oysters because oysters are one of Maryland's chief products.

An old man in Maryland once decided to test the world-wide legend that cattle kneel down in the barn at midnight on Christmas Eve and speak to one another. So he went out into the barn at midnight to listen. "Our poor old master won't last the year out," he heard one cow say to another. And in less than a week the man did die. Nowadays people do not eavesdrop on the cattle at midnight on Christmas Eve. No telling what one might hear, they say.

Maryland Negroes know the answer to why there is no such day as February 30. February 30 was Job's birthday, and when the poor man cried out in his sufferings, "Let the day perish whereon I was born," his prayer was answered.

Massachusetts

STATE FLOWER *mayflower (trailing arbutus)*

STATE BIRD *chickadee*

THE State of Massachusetts was named for its bay which was named by the Massachuset Indians, a tribe which occupied the coastal territory. The word *massachuset* means "at the range of hills," and refers to what are now the hills of Milton.

Nicknames: Baked Bean State; Bay State, or Old Bay State; Old Colony State; Puritan State

Massachusetts is called the Baked Bean State because all over Massachusetts the people eat baked beans for supper every Saturday night and again for Sunday breakfast. The custom began in the Puritan days when no work was done on Sunday, and in this way Sunday's dinner could be prepared on Saturday.

It is called the Bay State, or Old Bay State, for Massachusetts Bay, for which it was named. It is called the Old Colony State for the two original colonies which took root on its soil: Plymouth colony, settled by the Pilgrims, and Massachusetts Bay Colony, settled by the Puritans. It is sometimes called the Puritan State because Puritan philosophy dominated its development and still crops up sometimes in individual manifestations of the famous "New England conscience."

Massachusetts, though jokingly referred to as the "land of the bean and the cod," is in reality just that. The people still eat baked beans and brown bread every Saturday night and Sunday morning (as is done throughout most of New England), and the sacred cod hangs in the Massachusetts House of Representatives. This is a carved wooden codfish, four feet eleven inches long, painted to the life—the same one that was hung in the old State House in 1784, and maybe before that, "as a memorial of the importance of the Cod-Fishery to the welfare of this Commonwealth." Cape Cod is named for a big take of codfish recorded in "The Relation of Captain Gosnolf's Voyage, 1602," and codfish, stuffed and baked, was the original "Cape Cod turkey." Today the term is jokingly applied to salt codfish dished up in any form.

"One good dish of codfish" is one of the nine traditional musts
on the menu for the Forefathers' Feast celebrated annually on December 22. Forefathers' Feast commemorates the landing of the
Pilgrims, December 11, 1620—Old Style; and the first banquet in
honor of the Forefathers took place in Plymouth, Massachusetts, on
December 22, 1769. The eleven days' difference in date is the ad-
justment between the old and new calendars. On the menu for that
first memorial banquet was one large baked Indian whortleberry
pudding, one dish of *sauquetach* (pronounce it and you will recognize succotash), one dish of clams, one of oysters, one of eels, and
one good dish of codfish, a haunch of venison, a big apple pie, and
a round of cranberry tarts with cheese.

In addition to the food there were toasts, prayers, hymns, and

103

oratory. They toasted first the "forefathers," those first courageous settlers who stepped out of the little boat onto Plymouth Rock. They toasted John Carver, the first governor of Plymouth Colony, and all the succeeding governors; they toasted Miles Standish, and Robert Cushman, who preached the first sermon. And especially they toasted Massasoit, chief of the Wampanoag Indians, "our first and best friend," without whom the colonists could not have survived.

Massachusetts is probably the only state in the Union which uses the abbreviation *etc.* in a place name. But who wouldn't write Charco–etc.–maugg for a lake named Charcoggagogmanchau-gagogchabunagungamaugg?

Old jokes about the crooked streets of Boston still persist, and whoever jeers that they must have been laid out by the cows of the early settlers gets snubbed with the answer that Boston was never dead enough to be laid out.

Captain Kidd is said to be buried in King's Chapel churchyard in Boston. It is true that Kidd was in Boston in 1699 to deliver 1,111 ounces of gold and 2,353 ounces of silver to the governor, but how he got buried in a Boston churchyard after being hanged in London has never been explained. Acting on the knowledge that ghosts *have* to answer any question asked of them, several inquisitive souls have gone to Kidd's tomb at midnight, tapped on it three times, and made some inquiry. Not one ever received an answer, and this is why many people doubt that Captain Kidd is buried in King's Chapel churchyard in Boston.

Fall River is noted for the Lizzie Borden ax murder on August 4, 1892.

> Lizzie Borden took an ax,
> And gave her mother forty whacks.
> And when she saw what she had done,
> She gave her father forty-one.

Lizzie Borden was allegedly out in the barn when the murder actually took place; she was acquitted and lived to be sixty-seven years old. But the public thought she did it and still recites or sings the jingle with grim relish. There is a "Lizzie Borden Memorial Lecture" delivered annually in London to the British Society of Murder-Tasters, and there is a statue of Lizzie Borden in Fall River.

Cape Cod and Nantucket largely color the folklore of the state. On Cape Cod they used to measure the weather in blankets, they say; the nights were three or five or ten blankets cold. And on Nantucket whoever wanted to pluck a chicken for dinner could hold it out the door in one hand and a gale of wind would strip it down to the pinfeathers, all ready to clean. Some of the old town records show that whoever set up for being a weather prophet, and supposedly infallible, could be fined for falsely predicting fair weather.

Michigan

STATE FLOWER *apple blossom*

STATE BIRD *robin*

THERE has been much speculation about how the State of Michigan got its name, but it is generally believed that it bears the name of a tribe of Algonquian Indians, the Michigamea. The word means either big water or great lake.

Nicknames: Auto State, Lady of the Lakes, Lake State, Wolverine State

The most recent nickname for Michigan is the Auto State, dating from the immense development of automobile manufacturing in the state, especially at Detroit.

Michigan is called the Lady of the Lakes for its many inland lakes, and it is called the Lake State because it comprises two pen-

insulas lying in the arms of four of the five Great Lakes: Superior, Michigan, Huron, and Erie.

Michigan was nicknamed the Wolverine State for the great number of wolverines which formerly inhabited the territory. And the people are called Wolverines for their state, although one bit of false folk etymology advances the explanation that they used to eat wolf steak.

Michigan is a region of cold winters and high winds. The people of the Upper Peninsula describe their own climate as "ten months winter and two months late fall," or sometimes "ten months winter and two months poor sledding." There is a Michigan story that one winter when Paul Bunyan was camping at Manassee, the temperature dropped to 68° below zero and each degree was sixteen inches long. All the little flames in the camp lanterns froze solid,

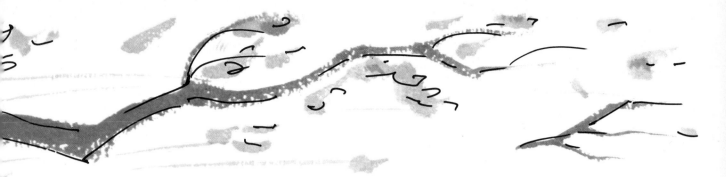

and the men could not blow them out. They did not want perpetual light in the bunkhouses, so they set the lanterns outside. In the spring they thawed out and flared up and set the whole northern Michigan woods on fire. In some parts of Michigan, however, the people cope with this situation better than that; when the flames in the lanterns freeze, they just break them off to put them out.

Michigan has its windy stories, too. A man was sitting on his back doorstep eating apple pie when a sudden high wind blew the house down and sailed the old fellow through the air into a tree. He grabbed a board which came flying by and held it over his face so he could finish his pie.

The folklore of Michigan is more than the folklore of weather. It is the folklore of the logging camps and lumberjacks, strong men and their feats, skid roads, shanty towns and shanty songs, of the men who sail the Great Lakes, and of the Tin Lizzie.

Beaver Island, in the northern end of Lake Michigan, twenty miles off the top end of the Lower Peninsula, is called "little Ireland." Here, until the helicopter changed the situation, the people received their mail in the winter by dog sled across the ice. Rival saloons on the island still hold singing competitions which last all night, and nobody wins; daybreak finds both sides still singing. The people still remember and sing the traditional ballads and songs of England and Ireland ("Lowlands, Low," "Old Erin," "The County Tyrone," etc.) and also many local originals with titles like "The Steam Tug Olsen," and "The Smugglers of Buffalo," and one called "Fisher Yankee Brown," who

> Once when beating down the Lake, he had to come about
> And heeled his schooner o'er so far he scooped up thirty
>   trout.

Paul Bunyan is said to have dug Lake Michigan (along with the other Great Lakes) as a drinking hole for his big blue ox. And certain old trees and orchards in southern Michigan are pointed to as having been planted by Johnny Appleseed, although there is no proof that Johnny Appleseed was ever in Michigan.

Minnesota

STATE FLOWER *lady's-slipper* (also called *moccasin flower, Indian shoe*)

STATE BIRD *goldfinch* (unofficial)

THE State of Minnesota was named for the Minnesota River. The word is a compound of two Dakota Indian words: *minni,* water, and *sota,* which is now, after long speculation, conceded to mean "sky-reflecting" or "sky-tinted."

Nicknames: Bread and Butter State, Gopher State, Lake State, North Star State

Minnesota is called the Bread and Butter State because of its wheat and dairy products, which supply this country with its bread and butter. The most common nickname is the Gopher State, for the little striped gopher which abounds in the Minnesota prairies. It is called the Lake State for its 10,000 lovely lakes. Among them is Itasca, where rises the great Mississippi. And Minnesota is called the North Star State because its seal bears the words *L'Etoile du Nord,* star of the north. The people are called Gophers because they inhabit the Gopher State.

Minnesota contains the westernmost seaport of the Atlantic Ocean: Duluth! It contains the biggest man-made hole in the world: the open iron-ore mine at Hibbing, occupying 1,250 acres; it contains the only road on earth ever paved with iron, and the coldest spot in the United States: the town of Bemidji. The Paul

Bunyan Winter Carnival takes place in Bemidji every year, centered around the Paul Bunyan logging stories and the fifteen-ton concrete statue of Paul. This is the region in which they claim that every time Paul shod the blue ox, they had to open up another Minnesota iron mine.

There are many stories claiming that, in spite of the advances of man-made urban civilization, bears still wander into Duluth in the spring and rummage through the garbage pails in people's back yards. One is said to have sauntered into a Duluth hotel lobby, but there is no information as to whether or not he got accommodations.

Mississippi

STATE FLOWER   *magnolia*

STATE BIRD   *mockingbird*

THE State of Mississippi was named for its great river, and the river was named by the Indians of the region (perhaps the Ojibwa). They called it *misi,* great or big, *sipi,* river or water.

Nicknames: Bayou State, Eagle State, Magnolia State, Mud-cat State

Mississippi is called the Bayou State because of its many bayous, which are little river branches in the delta. It is sometimes referred to as the Eagle State because its state coat of arms bears an American eagle. Its most popular nickname is Magnolia State for its abundance of magnolia trees. Sometimes it is jokingly called the Mud-cat State because its swamps and muddy rivers teem with big catfish which wallow in the mud, and are therefore popularly called mud-cats. The people too are often nicknamed Mud-cats. Another nickname for the people of Mississippi is Tadpoles, because it is said that they live half their lives under water.

Everybody who lives along the Mississippi believes there is magic in its yellow water. Mark Twain (in *Life on the Mississippi*) said yaller Mississippi water was wholesomer than any clear water anywhere. If the sediment settles in the pitcher, he said, *stir it up!*

One drink of the Mississippi River makes the drinker return to it. The unlucky have a change of luck if they wash in it, and it beautifies the faces of women. That is why all Mississippi women are beautiful, they say. And if you are bewitched or conjured, just hire a little boat and row across the river, and the spell will be broken.

Like many another of the United States, Mississippi has its mosquito stories, too. The ones along the river, for instance, are so vicious that they torment the alligators to death. There is a story about two Mississippi mosquitoes who carried off a full-grown man between them. "Shall we eat him here or take him to the swamp?" one of them said to the other.

"Let's eat him here, or those big mosquitoes in the swamp will take him away from us."

Some Mississippi Negroes, and some white people, too, in that state, still practice the charming rite of the birth tree. A young tree is planted for a baby at his birth (or a tree already growing is chosen) and named for him. If a tree already growing is chosen, it is watered with the infant's first bath water, and "that makes 'em kin." Thereafter they share the same fate; the welfare of the tree and the welfare of the child are believed to be bound up together. If misfortune befalls one, it befalls the other. If one dies, the other dies.

There is little or no folklore about mermaids in Mississippi, but there is one small coastal town where mermaids jump out of the bushes and hop onto the radiators of passing automobiles. Perhaps this is why some tourists come home with fancy radiator caps.

What is it has four eyes and runs over 2,000 miles? *The Mississippi River.*

Missouri

STATE FLOWER *hawthorn, or red haw*

STATE BIRD *bluebird*

THE State of Missouri was named for the river, which was probably named by early French explorers for a tribe of Indians, the Missouri, who lived along its southern banks. The name means "dugout canoes," or "wooden canoes." Thus the Missouri Indians were "the people using dugout canoes." (A dugout canoe is one made by hollowing out a whole tree trunk or log.)

The word *missouri* does not mean muddy water, as was formerly supposed. The Missouri Indians did call their river "muddy water," but it was another word, *pekitanoui*.

Nicknames: Iron Mountain State, Lead State, Ozark State, Puke State, Show Me State

Missouri is sometimes referred to as the Iron Mountain State for Iron Mountain in St. Francois County, which contains rich veins of iron ore. It is called the Lead State for the lead mines in its southeastern section. It is called the Ozark State for the Ozark Mountains which characterize the region south of the Missouri River.

There are three explanations of how Missouri came to be called the Puke State. One is that the name dates from 1827 when great hordes of Missourians began to pour across the state line into the Galena lead mines, and those already there said Missouri had puked. California also takes credit for calling Missouri immigrants Pukes; there were so many coming across the plains, they said, it looked as if they were "vomited forth." Another story softens the nickname with the theory that Puke is a corruption of Pike, because the first Missouri immigrants into California were from Pike County.

Missouri began to be called the Show Me State after a speech made by a Missouri congressman in 1899 when he said, "I'm from Missouri and you've got to *show me.*"

The State of Missouri is like one of its own big Missouri mules: "the state with the kick to it," so says John Gunther in *Inside USA*. Missouri is the South (so much so that one section is called Little Dixie), and Missouri is the Middle West, full of corn-crop tales. In the agricultural counties north of the Missouri River lies a great corn-growing region.

> They have yarns—
> Of one corn crop in Missouri when the roots
> Went so deep and drew off so much water
> The Mississippi river bed that year was dry.*

And south of the Missouri River lie the isolated Ozark Mountains—a world apart, where old folk beliefs about planting and farming and cures, love tests and love potions and love charms still govern daily life.

> To grow good peppers you have to be angry while planting
> them.
> Eggs set on Sunday will hatch all roosters.
> A dream dreamed on Friday will come true.
> Carry a hog's tooth to prevent toothache.
> Bend a mullein stalk toward your beloved's house. If she loves
> you, the stalk will straighten again and revive; if she
> loves another, the mullein will die.
> If you watch your lover out of sight, he will never come back.

---

* From Carl Sandburg's *The People, Yes,* Harcourt, Brace, 1936. By permission of the publishers.

Montana

STATE FLOWER   *bitterroot*

STATE BIRD   *western meadowlark*

THE State of Montana is named for its mountains, from the Latin *montana,* meaning mountainous regions.

Nicknames: Bonanza State, Stubtoe State, Treasure State

Montana is called the Bonanza State and Treasure State for the same reason—its rich mines. It is called the Stubtoe State because of the rough going in its mountainous sections. Montana is big—as big as Indiana, Illinois, and Michigan put together—and is in-

habited by very few people. In fact, there are 10,000 more people lying in coffins in the city of Butte than there are walking around.

Western Montana means mines (copper, silver, gold); it means Butte, the miners and their lore. Eastern Montana means plains and wheat and huge cattle and sheep ranches. Primitive Montana means vast areas set aside by the government to preserve the mountain forests, in which not even a road is allowed.

The city of Butte is described as being "a mile deep," because it sits on top of some 2,800 miles of mine shafts and tunnels. It has been called the toughest town in the United States. Many another town calls itself the toughest, but Butte, the city of miners, must be granted its own special toughness. Men engaged in tough and dangerous work are usually given to violent recreations.

Butte has also been called the singing town. The miners used to sing at their work underground; they sang in the streets, and they

sang in the saloons at night. But unfortunately the wonderful singing underground has passed away, for the human voice cannot compete with modern percussion drills. But the old songs like

> My sweetheart's the mule in the mine,
> I drive her with only one line,

and

> Nothing could be finer,
> Than to be a dirty miner,
> In the mo–o–o–orning,

and many others will never die. The miners are proud of their dirty clothes and regard them as the badge of severe and dangerous work that only supermen can perform.

A large part of Montana folklore is sheepherding lore. There are stories about sheepherders who, hearing only the bleating of sheep year in and year out, cannot even say Montana without bleating themselves. If you ask them where they come from, they say Montaa–aa–naa–aa.

Nebraska

STATE FLOWER *goldenrod*

STATE BIRD *western meadowlark*

THE State of Nebraska is named for the big spreading or dividing river (now called the North Platte and South Platte rivers) which is said to have been named either by the Omaha Indians *ni*, water, *ubthatka*, spreading, or by the Oto Indians, *Nebrathka*, which also means flat or spreading water.

Nicknames: Antelope State, Blackwater State, Bug-eating State, Cornhusker State, Tree Planters State

Nebraska used to be called the Antelope State for the many beautiful antelope which formerly grazed and ran across its prairies. It is called the Blackwater State because its rich soil colors the water of its running streams. It is called the Bug-eating State for the many bull-bats (a local term for nighthawks) which eat flying insects at twilight. The official nickname is Tree Planters State because, in the words of the 1895 Nebraska legislature, "Nebraska is pre-eminently a tree-planting state." The nickname Cornhusker State is fairly recent, having been extended to the state from the football team of the University of Nebraska. The people of Nebraska are facetiously called either Bug-eaters or Cornhuskers.

The Nebraska state capitol has a statue called the Sower on top of the dome: fitting symbol of a state famous for its wheat, corn, hay, and alfalfa. Nebraska's early legends are about hardy, courageous people, "the sod-house settlers," who staked out their homesteads across a treeless land. There were no trees with which to build log cabins; sod houses were what they *had to have*—small houses built with blocks of turf, or sod, piled one upon the other. They made their fences this way, too; and it is said that the phrase "ugly as a mud fence" springs from this locale, because nothing looks worse than a mud fence after a hard rain, with its runnels and washed-out places and untidy grass roots sticking out.

The story of the Nebraska sod-house settlers is a series of weather tales—droughts, scorching heat unrelieved by rain, blizzards, and bitter cold, hailstorms, cyclones, prairie fires, and plagues of insects (grasshoppers, fleas, centipedes). Nebraska is the state in which one famous cyclone picked up some wagon ruts and dropped them over to the north in South Dakota in a spot no wagon road had ever been before. But in spite of losing their crops to the grasshoppers summer after summer for nineteen years (1856–1875), somehow the people stuck it out and prospered. Today they are still at the mercy of the weather, with few trees and no hills to give them shelter. When Nebraska gets weather, Nebraska gets 100 per cent plus of whatever the weather is.

Nevada

STATE FLOWER   *sagebrush* (unofficial)

STATE BIRD   *mountain bluebird* (unofficial)

THE State of Nevada is named for the snow-capped mountain range on its western border, the Sierra Nevada Mountains. These in turn were named for the Sierra Nevadas in Spain. The word *sierra* is the Spanish word for saw; our word *serrate,* saw-toothed, comes from the same root. *Nevado* means snow-covered.

Nicknames: Battle-born State, Mining State, Sagebrush State, Sage-hen State, Silver State

Nevada is called the Battle-born State because it was admitted to the Union (1864) during the Civil War. It is called the Mining State for its wealth of silver, gold, copper, lead, zinc, mercury, tungsten, antimony, and manganese mines. It is called the Sage-brush State for the sage which grows wild all over it, and it is called the Sage-hen State because sage hens were formerly abundant. Nevada is called the Silver State for the rich strikes of silver ore for which it is famous. The people of Nevada are referred to as Sage-hens or Diggers or Miners.

Nevada contains fewer people than any other state in the Union. One inhabitant per square mile is about what Nevada has. Nevada lore is mostly mining lore (especially silver mining), ranch lore, and gambling lore. The stories one reads and hears all say that nobody ever got into a fight for himself in Nevada; he just jumped in to help out the fellow who was getting the worst of it. How that fellow got into it is not explained. Yet in the old days a man could get a life sentence for stealing a horse and only three years for murder.

There are fabulous tales in Nevada about silver mines half a mile under the earth and stories of rich strikes and lost mines and lost treasure. There is a stretch of Death Valley in southern Nevada where the people say, "It isn't the humidity, it's the heat," and where the burros kick holes in the two-inch water pipes (which lie on the surface between the springs and the mines) and drink where they please rather than trudge two or three miles in the heat to the water holes.

The little lakes into which Nevada rivers empty their waters are called sinks because they have no visible outlets. The rivers empty into them and apparently just sink into the earth. Local legend explains them thus: the day the Creator finished creating the Great Lakes and the Missouri and Mississippi rivers, he had in mind to make the biggest river of all for Nevada. So he made eight nice rivers which were to be branches for the great big one. By then it was night and too dark to finish, so he just tucked the ends in for overnight and then forgot to come back and finish.

New Hampshire

STATE FLOWER *purple lilac*

STATE BIRD *purple finch* (unofficial)

NEW HAMPSHIRE was named for the county of Hampshire in England. A large portion of the territory which is now New Hampshire was given to Captain John Mason by patent from the council of Plymouth in 1629, and he named it for his old home in England.

Nicknames: Granite State, Mother of Rivers, White Mountain State

New Hampshire is called the Granite State for its great granite mountains and quarries. It is called the Mother of Rivers because five New England rivers rise in the New Hampshire mountains. And it is called the White Mountain State for the White Mountains in the northern part of the state. It is the beauty of these mountains, invaded by tourists all summer and by city skiers in the winter, that gives New Hampshire the name "the Switzerland of America." The people of New Hampshire are referred to as Granite Boys.

The "north country" of New Hampshire is the township of Pittsburg, where until recently the people could sing folk songs eight hours at a stretch without getting through the repertoire. One song entitled "Maggie Gray" has 200 verses, and it was a point of honor with every old-timer in the region to know the whole thing by heart. How many still know it? It would be nice to find out. Today the young people don't sing, the old-timers complain; they play bridge instead. One of the special songs of the region is about an old scalawag of the Day family named Dan: "If 'twant for his failings he'd be quite a man."

There is a charming record of a school feast which took place in colonial New Hampshire about 1790. All winter the children saved the wood ashes from the big fireplace which heated the one-room school, and sold them to a near-by potash works. With the money they had a school treat, to which they invited parents, the teacher, and the minister. For refreshments they served rum, raisins, and gingerbread.

It must be easy to have a turkey dinner in New Hampshire. Old Man Moses got up in the dark of one cold fall morning to go into the woods for firewood. As he was going along he saw twelve wild turkeys sitting in a row on the limb of a tree which overhung a pond. If he went home for his gun, he thought, they would be gone when he got back; so he decided to throw his ax—and maybe hit *one*. He threw the ax, but instead of hitting a turkey it struck the limb of the tree, split it lengthwise, and cracked it off into the water. The twelve turkeys were caught by their toes in the crack! Old Man Moses jumped into the pond to drag his catch ashore. His big old jumper coat spread out around him as he swam. He got the tree limb and the twelve turkeys all right, and when he got ashore discovered that his shirt and coat sleeves were full of fish. Not bad for a morning's haul. The people around Peterborough, New Hampshire, when they tell this story, declare that it is just as true now as it ever was.

New Jersey

STATE FLOWER   *violet*

STATE BIRD   *goldfinch*

THE State of New Jersey was named in 1664 by Sir George Carteret, one of the original proprietors of the grant, for his native island of Jersey.

Nicknames: Clam State; Garden State; Jersey Blue State; Mosquito State; New Spain, or State of Spain

New Jersey is called the Clam State for the prodigious number of clams dug on its shores. It is called the Garden State (officially) because so much Jersey business is in truck farming and flowers for city markets. It got the nickname Jersey Blue State during the American Revolution when the state militia wore blue uniforms. It is called the Mosquito State because the New Jersey marshes produce some of the most vicious mosquitoes in the world. New Jersey was formerly called New Spain, or the State of Spain, because, in local Jersey legend, in 1812 Joseph Bonaparte, then still king of Spain, took refuge in New Jersey and built a fine mansion at Bordentown. The people are called Clam-catchers sometimes, sometimes Jersey Blues, and sometimes Spaniards.

New Jersey is a northern hilly region with narrow, fertile, farm-land valleys. It is the tidal marshes east of Newark and the hobo jungles on the Newark dumps. It is the famous Jersey shore, warmed by Gulf Stream waters and studded with sand bars and summer resorts. It is spring bursting forth on Cape May while Bayonne youngsters are still sledding. And it is the great wasteland across the southern part of the state, known as "the Pines," with dazzling white sand roads through dark woods of scrub oak and pine, inhabited by the Pineys.

The Pineys are the people of this sandy, scrub-pine region whose two hundred years or more of isolation have given them a distinctive local speech and way of life. Big Sea Day used to be a Piney celebration. On the second Sunday in August every year whole families used to emerge from the Pines in horse-drawn buggies and

wagons for an annual bath in the sea, in the neighborhood of Sea-girt. They went into the water fully clothed in whatever they happened to be wearing, and dried off in the sun. But Big Sea Day is a thing of the past, since the Jersey shore has filled up with summer resorts and gone commercial.

Summer resorts have not scared away the Jersey ghosts, however. A golden-haired lady ghost still haunts the sands around Cape May. A headless man, carrying his head under one arm, still stalks the dunes at Barnegat. The story is that he was one of Captain Kidd's men, beheaded by Captain Kidd himself for trying to loot the common treasure. Hidden treasure in several spots along the Jersey shores is guarded by a crew of ghostly sailors, some still dressed in sailor togs and some just dancing in their bones. "Kidd's tree" near Sandy Hook is the scene of some well-reported ghostly revels.

123

New Mexico

STATE FLOWER   *yucca*

STATE BIRD   *road runner*

NEW MEXICO was named as long ago as 1583 by the Spanish explorer Antonio de Espejo for the old Mexico which he had already seen.

Nicknames: Cactus State, Sunshine State, Spanish State

New Mexico is called the Cactus State because its plains are covered with cactus, and the Sunshine State for its almost perpetual sunshine. It is called the Spanish State because such a large proportion of its people speak Spanish. It is the only state in the Union which has two official languages: English and Spanish.

Pecos Bill staked out New Mexico, the stories say, and dug the Rio Grande. Although New Mexico was not admitted to the Union until 1912, this land of broken mesas and wide deserts, cattle ranches, and vast sheepherding stretches is the most anciently settled of all the United States. Santa Fe, the capital, is the oldest capital city in the United States; it was founded in 1609 by the Spanish. New Mexico, home of thousands of Pueblo Indians and their beautiful, ancient stone or adobe storied pueblos (*pueblo* means village), is also the birthplace of the atom bomb.

In New Mexico sheepherders' lore the morning star is called *La Estrella del Pastor,* the Shepherd's Star, because the shepherd has to be awake and on duty when it rises.

One of the sheep stories New Mexicans like to tell to outsiders is about a man who owned many sheep. He lived by a river, and on the other side of the river grew thick green grass, much thicker and greener and more plentiful than the grass on his own side of the river. So he decided to build a bridge across the river so that his sheep could get to the wonderful grass on the other side. But when the bridge was finished, he found he had made it so narrow that only one sheep at a time could get across. Then the sheep began to cross the bridge: one—two—three—four—

A long silence falls. The listener waits, and finally may say, "Well—go on!" But the teller answers, "Wait! Wait till all those sheep get across the bridge!"

New Mexico breeds its own proverbs too, and since 90 per cent of the state is ranch country, the proverbs have a ranch-life flavor: "When you've come to the end of your rope, tie a knot in it and hang on!"

New York

STATE FLOWER *rose*

STATE BIRD *bluebird* (unofficial)

THE little Dutch city of New Amsterdam on Manhattan Island was named New York in 1664 when all the Dutch holdings in America became English property. The territory was granted by the king of England to his brother, the Duke of York, and New Amsterdam was renamed in his honor. Some authorities hold that both the state and the city were named for the county of Yorkshire in England.

Nicknames: Empire State, Excelsior State, Knickerbocker State

New York is called the Empire State because of its "commanding position" and its wealth. It is called the Excelsior State for its motto, *Excelsior,* which means higher (from Latin *excelsus,* high, superior). It is called the Knickerbocker State in memory of the first Dutch settlers and the typical wide breeches worn by them. Washington Irving's character Diedrich Knickerbocker, fictitious author of *A History of New York,* made the term so popular that the people of New York are still called Knickerbockers.

New York lore is the lore of ghosts and buried treasure in the Hudson Valley, of pirates and buried treasure and shipwrecks on Long

126

Island, the phantom ships of the Hudson River, the sunken treasure ship in the East River off the end of Fifty-third Street, anecdotes and legends of the old Erie Canal boating days, Niagara honeymoon jokes, and the songs of the state (traditional and local).

They have a new, or maybe it is an old, way of catching winter rabbits in the northern part of New York State. A man takes a bright light out into his pasture and sets it down on the ground. The rabbits are attracted to the light and sit around and look at it. The glare makes their eyes water; the water flows out of their eyes and falls to the ground and freezes. Soon an icicle forms, an ever-increasing icicle, from their eyes to the ground. And thus the rabbits are frozen fast to the ground "right where they be." All the man has to do in the morning is go out and pick them up.

New York gave Santa Claus to America, and "Yankee Doodle" and Rip Van Winkle. Santa Claus came to the New World with the early Dutch settlers of Manhattan Island. He was their *Sant Nikolaas,* Saint Nicholas. People gradually dropped the "ni" and said "Santa Klaas." In colonial days he used to go around giving out presents on Saint Nicholas Day (December 6) riding a white horse and dressed in a three-cornered hat, Dutch knickerbockers, and shoes with silver buckles.

"Yankee Doodle" was born at Fort Crailo, Rensselaer, New York, about 1775, when a British army surgeon made up a lot of nonsense verses to ridicule the ragamuffin American troops. They sang it to an old, old tune (English, Irish, Dutch, Spanish—no one knows for sure). But the ragamuffin Yankees knew a good jaunty thing when they heard it, took it to themselves with pride and glee, and turned the tables on the British by playing it back to them when they surrendered at Yorktown in 1781.

The story of Rip Van Winkle and his magic sleep of twenty years is an old European tale transplanted to a little Dutch colonial village in the Catskills and its ne'er-do-well town character, and made famous by Washington Irving in his *Sketch Book.*

New York lore is also the folklore of New York City, which is folklore around the globe. It ranges from Chinatown dragon parades, colorful Italian street fiestas, the songs, foods, and feasts of more than eighty ethnic groups throughout the city, to the speech ways of Brooklyn and the Bronx, and Harlem rent-party lore and Harlem music. It is subway and taxi-driver lore and anecdote, children's sidewalk games and rimes and chants and insults and gags, new wine in old jingles.

> Mary had a little lamb,
> Its fleece was white as snow,
> And everywhere that Mary went,
> She took a bus.

The Music Division of the New York Public Library lists more than 200 songs *about* New York City.

New York City lore is the lore of its street names too: Maiden Lane, as crooked as the little stream which first marked its course, where rosy-cheeked young Dutch maidens gathered to wash their linens; Old Slip, where the wonderful smell of roasting coffee still greets the nose; Patchin Place, Pomander Walk, Shinbone Alley, Sniffen Court, and Smell Street (which is now called Broad).

New York City lore is the skyscrapers and the lights and ferryboats, the big trucks which go around town every day eating up garbage, the horse-drawn victorias and hansoms across Fifty-ninth Street from the Plaza, which will take you jogging through Central Park. It is penny arcades and shooting galleries and flea circuses on West Forty-second Street, teen-age-gang lingos, and other special lingos of little groups and little worlds, which change as fast as they can be interpreted.

It is also the lost and charming old cries of the street vendors, forbidden since 1908. The street cries were banned in a campaign against noise and nuisance. But occasionally one still hears the scissors-grinder man: "Scis-sors' to grind." In some sections the banana man with his pushcart still calls his musical "Ba-na-nas'." And the springtime flower cart of Greenwich Village, drawn by a horse with flowers in his ears, has a vendor who cries, "Fresh' flowers!"

North Carolina

STATE FLOWER *dogwood*

STATE BIRD *cardinal*

THE region called Carolina originally lay between the northern latitudes 31–36° and reached from the Atlantic coast to the Mississippi River. King Charles I of England named it for himself when he gave it to Sir Robert Heath in 1629; and the lands were incorporated into a province, then spelled Carolana. But even as long ago as 1562 the French explorer Jean Ribaut named this territory Carolina for the little boy-king of France, Charles IX. The division into North and South Carolina was made by the Lords Proprietors in 1665.

Nicknames: Old North State, Tarheel State, Turpentine State

North Carolina began to be called the Old North State when the original tract of Carolina was divided. It earned the nickname Tarheel State during the Civil War when one brigade of North Carolina soldiers held their position alone in terrible conflict, while their supporters had to retreat. When the battle was over someone asked the victors, "Any more tar down there where you come from, boys?"

"Not a drop!" was the retort. "Old Jeff has sent for it all to tar you'uns heels, so you can stick out the next fight."

Thus Tarheel has been a proud epithet ever since.

And North Carolina is called the Turpentine State because its pines produce great amounts of turpentine.

The people are called Tarheels or Tarheelers, sometimes Tar Boilers, and sometimes Tuckoes or Tuckahoes. *Tuckahoe* is Indian bread. The term is applied to the root (edible only if cooked) of two species of arum, but *especially* to a certain underground fungus found on the roots of trees, which looks like a loaf of bread: white inside with a brown crust. The settlers learned about this from the

Indians, and the name came to be applied to the poor people of North Carolina (and lower Virginia) who ate it gratefully when food was scarce. Now any North Carolinian is facetiously called a Tuckahoe.

The folklore of North Carolina is, of course, the folklore of the South, which does not differ much from state to state. In North Carolina, as elsewhere in the South, people still bury their dead so that the corpse faces east; those who believe in ghosts believe also that wire screens will keep them out; a rabbit's foot tied around the baby's neck will help him cut his teeth more easily; and, like other Southerners, the people shoot off fireworks for Christmas. But *only* in North Carolina did the John Kuners prance and sing for Christmas, to the accompaniment of bones and horns. The John Kuners were a group of Negroes (the number varied: ten, twelve, twenty) dressed in "tatters," which were strips of bright-colored cloth or ribbons sewed to their pants and jackets. They wore fantastic masks called "kuner faces." And they went from house to house, dancing and singing:

Hah! Low!
Here we go!
Hah! Low!
KUNERS COMIN'.

They danced and sang for the spectators, passed round a hat for pennies, and went on. This old custom was called "kunering," and came to North Carolina with a group of slaves from the Bahamas. Scholars have traced the custom back to a religious rite of the Gold Coast, West Africa. But kunering is a legend today; the merry crew is not seen any more.

All over the world, in fairy tale and in real life, it is said that a young girl must do certain things before she is fit to be married. In some places she had to spin a certain amount of yarn or weave a certain amount of cloth or hem twelve tablecloths. In North Carolina, no girl was ready for marriage until she knew what it meant to pick a certain amount of cotton. Even in very wealthy families, she had to pick at least a shoeful.

131

North Dakota

STATE FLOWER *prairie rose*

STATE BIRD *western meadowlark*

THE Dakotas were named for the Dakota Indians, who were formerly spread through that region. The word means "allies" or "friends" in their language. Dakota Territory was created in 1861, and the division into North Dakota and South Dakota as two separate states came in 1889 when both were admitted to the Union.

Nicknames: Flickertail State, Sioux State, Land of the Dakotas

North Dakota is called the Flickertail State because it abounds in the little flickertail ground squirrel. It is called the Sioux State or Land of the Dakotas for the Dakota Indians, who were called Sioux by enemy tribes. *Sioux* is short for *Nadouessioux,* the Chippewa word for "adders" or "enemies," which came to us through the French.

The wrong-side-up story is probably the most famous of all North Dakota legends. This is the story of a North Dakota pioneer who started his first spring sowing one fine day in 1883; he was preparing to plant wheat. As he worked he realized that an old Dakota Indian was watching him as he broke through the prairie grass and turned it under. Finally, when he stopped to rest for a moment, the old man approached, examined the furrow, and picked up a clod of the buried grass.

"Wrong side up," he said, and laid it back with the grass side up. Then he walked away without further comment.

White men told this story for years as a joke on the Indian and his ignorance of plowing. Today the white man knows that the old Dakota man was right. The prairies should *not* have been plowed up. The big winds came and blew some forty million acres of good Dakota soil over into Indiana and Ohio. And today there is a statue in North Dakota of this old Indian of unknown name, honoring his wisdom.

Ohio

STATE FLOWER *red carnation*

STATE BIRD *cardinal*

THE State of Ohio was named for its river the Ohio, which used to be called the Main Street of the nation because, with its keelboat and packet-boat traffic, it *was* the main highway of this country for many years. The meaning of the word Ohio is variously explained by many writers. One offers an Iroquois Indian word, *oheo,* meaning "beautiful," or *ohuipeekhanne,* meaning "a stream with white froth"; another proposes *ohion-hiio* (also Iroquois) meaning "beautiful river."

Nicknames: Buckeye State, Yankee State

Ohio is called the Buckeye State because it has many buckeye chestnut trees. It is called the Yankee State because it was largely settled by people from New England and by veterans of the American Revolution. Some people say that Southerners first called it the Yankee State because of its free institutions. The people are nicknamed Buckeyes.

The folklore of Ohio is very much the lore of the Ohio River and the roistering keelboatmen like Mike Fink and his ilk. The real Eliza of *Uncle Tom's Cabin,* fleeing the slave-searchers and their bloodhounds with her child in her arms, crossed the Ohio River on

134

the ice at Ripley. She was welcomed and cared for in the house of a Reverend John Rankins, whose house is still shown as one of the stations of the underground railroad.

Farmers' children in Ohio still collect "luck eggs." These are the little undersized eggs found in hens' nests at the end of the laying season. The children still make a wish on first seeing a newborn calf. If the neighbor's cat comes listening around a house, people know it is listening for gossip and take it as a sign that the owner of the cat gossips about them.

In the summer, like children all over this country, Ohio children catch a grasshopper and chant, "Spit, spit, spit tobacco juice" until it does. It doesn't take long.

Everywhere in America people carry various things in their pockets to ward off, cure, or absorb rheumatism: a potato, a haddock bone (Newfoundland), a pig's tooth, a lodestone, a nutmeg, a walnut. But natives of the Buckeye State bank on a buckeye in the pocket to keep them free of rheumatism.

What is round at both ends and high in the middle? *Ohio.*

Oklahoma

STATE FLOWER *mistletoe*

STATE BIRD *scissor-tailed flycatcher*

THE State of Oklahoma got its name from two Choctaw Indian words: *okla*, meaning "people," and *homma*, meaning "red." The term was first used in the Choctaw-Chickasaw Treaty (1866) with the United States, which named this intertribal commonwealth the Territory of Oklahoma.

Nicknames: Sooner State, Boomer's Paradise

Oklahoma is called the Sooner State because many homesteaders arrived there sooner than the legal date set. At twelve noon on April 22, 1889, a gun was fired permitting some 20,000 settlers, lined up at the border, to stream across the patrolled line into unassigned lands to stake out homestead claims. Those who sneaked over to grab the best sites sooner than the assigned moment were called Sooners. But it is also often said that Oklahoma is the state where they'd sooner tell a good story than be accurate.

Oklahoma is called the Boomer's Paradise because when the territory was opened up for white settlement, thousands of boomers poured into the region. A boomer, in this sense of the word, is any one of a rush of settlers into new territory.

136

Every one of the United States brags about having either the best weather or the worst weather in the nation. But Oklahoma probably has the most famous weather of them all. Oklahoma rain, for instance, is a dust storm. Northwestern Oklahoma comprises part of our notorious dust bowl. Oklahoma is the kind of country where a man can die of sunstroke in the morning, and his neighbor can freeze to death that night. Sometimes a hot day gets cold so fast that the frogs get stuck with their heads sticking up out of the ice.

Oklahoma people like to show outsiders the "crowbar holes" in their houses. The crowbar hole is a hole in the wall through which they shove a crowbar to test the wind. If the crowbar bends, the wind is normal; if it breaks, it is not safe to go out.

Oklahoma, once Indian Territory, is still the Indian state. Fifty-seven tribes of North American Indians are represented in Oklahoma. And one of the loveliest stories to come out of that state is the story of the bed on the mountain.

The Southern Cheyenne Indians finally settled on a reservation taking in part of the valley of the North Canadian River. In the early days, the Cheyenne, like other Indians, bitterly resented the influx of white settlers into their territory; and this resentment gave rise to the hope and belief in a messiah who would come and deliver them and their lands from the white men. In the year 1890 the Cheyenne made great preparations for the coming of their messiah. They held many great meetings and ceremonies on top of Coyote Butte, whose beautiful white dolomite ledges rise high above the North Canadian River.

One morning after a prolonged night gathering of the Cheyenne on Coyote Butte, people saw a bed, high on the Butte against the sky. It was a white iron bed, equipped with good springs and mattress and piled with warm Indian blankets.

When asked why the bed was there, one of the old Cheyenne sages answered that it was for the messiah. When the white man's messiah came to this world he had no place to sleep; he had to lie in a stable. When the Cheyenne messiah arrived, he would find a good bed.

137

Oregon

STATE FLOWER *Oregon grape*

STATE BIRD *western meadowlark*

SEVERAL explanations of the name of Oregon have been advanced. One is that it was named for the wild marjoram (Spanish, *orégano*); but this is not likely because Spanish coastal explorers and adventurers of the sixteenth century did not call the region Oregon. Possibly the state was named for its fabulous Oregon River, which, it was said, flowed westward and would guide travelers to the wealth of the Orient. Another is that the Oregon River had its source in western Minnesota, and because it flowed through a tornado region was called *Ouragan* (hurricane) by the French. Still another theory is that the word oregon comes from a Shoshone Indian word *oyerungon,* meaning "place of plenty."

Nicknames: Beaver State; Hard-case State, or Land of Hard Cases; Sunset State; Webfoot State

Oregon is called the Beaver State because it formerly abounded in beaver, and the famous early white fur traders made their wealth in beaver furs. It is called the Hard-case State, or Land of Hard Cases, for the rough, tough life its settlers had to survive. (A "hard case" is a rough, tough person.) It is called the Sunset State because its lands jut so far to the west, and it is called the Webfoot State for its damp climate and heavy rainfall. They say that Oregon people have run around in the wet so long, now, that their babies are born web-footed. The people of Oregon are called Beavers or Hard Cases or Webfeet.

But the basic folklore of Oregon is many things: the tales and the lore of the early fur traders, of the 3,000 emigrants who entered the region via the Oregon Trail. It is the lore of the Yankee seafaring traders who rounded Cape Horn and founded the coastal cities.

It is said that a man from Portland, Maine, and a man from Boston tossed a coin to see who would have the naming of the city now called Portland, and the man from Maine won. It is the lure, as well as the lore, of the vast, wild, lonely, and still unknown tracts of eastern Oregon, where the little hamlets lie 150 miles apart.

It is today's logging lore as well as the tales of yesterday's "timber-beasts," as the old-time loggers were called. Paul Bunyan was in Oregon. The only difference between the modern logger and the old-timer is that today one man can handle *three* 200-foot logs at a time, with the help of the huge, powerful machines which are as fabulous as Paul's Blue Ox. Logging today involves just as much hard work, danger, fighting, drinking, daring, bragging, and cussing as ever—and as many tall tales. And it is just as true today as ever that Oregon loggers never shave; they pound their whiskers in with a hammer and bite them off on the inside.

The Oregon logger calls the Oregon farmer an "appleknocker." And he has a special definition for the word "catty": catty means agile, light-footed, and clever. Every good logger has to be catty. "To lower the boom" means to knock out a man in a fight with one punch. A "splinter-picker" is a sawmill worker. An excessive bragger is called a "young robin" because he is all mouth and no tail!

Pennsylvania

STATE FLOWER   *mountain laurel*

STATE BIRD   *ruffed grouse*

THE State of Pennsylvania was named by King Charles II of England in 1681 in honor of William Penn's father. William Penn himself had thought to name it New Wales because the region was "hilly, pretty country" like the old Wales. But Pennsylvania it became. William Penn was deeply troubled in his mind about this "lest it should be looked upon as a vanity" in himself, and not interpreted as the king's respect for his father. The word is popularly thought to mean "Penn's woods," but actually it means "wooded hills," from the Welsh word *pen,* which means "head, headland, hill," and *sylvania,* from Latin, *silvanus,* forest, woods.

State Lore

Nicknames: Coal State, Keystone State, Oil State, Quaker State,
Steel State

The nicknames Coal State, Oil State, Steel State speak for themselves; Pennsylvania is called any one of these three names because of her wealth in these three products. Among the stories about the nickname Keystone State, one is that when the old Pennsylvania Avenue Bridge was built over Rock Creek, connecting Washington, D.C. and Georgetown, the initials of the thirteen original states were carved in the stones of the arch. The initials of Pennsylvania appeared in the keystone of the arch. Another story is that John Morton of Pennsylvania cast the last vote for the Declaration of Independence, thereby causing Pennsylvania's to be the thirteenth or the keystone vote.

Pennsylvania is called the Quaker State because William Penn, its proprietor, was a member of the Society of Friends, the people called Quakers. Pennsylvanians are nicknamed either Pennamites or Quakers for William Penn and the early Quaker settlers.

Pennsylvania, headquarters for the oil, steel, and coal industries of the nation, and boasting ten big industrial cities, is still half forest! The most famous of the ten big cities is Philadelphia: birthplace of the nation, say the history books, because here is the Liberty Bell; here stands the little house where Betsy Ross made the first American flag; and here were born the Declaration of Independence and the Constitution of the United States.

Pennsylvania folk heroes are Joe Magarac, the Hungarian hero of the steel mills; Gib Morgan, creator and hero of oil-field song and story; Hungry Sam Miller, who once ate 144 fried eggs, 200 oysters, and 48 pies; and Haywire Mac (McClintock), famous railroad boomer who wrote and sang "The Big Rock Candy Mountains." A *boomer* is an itinerant railroad worker, restless and wandering, who changes habitually from one road and one job to another. The Big Rock Candy Mountains are boomer paradise and hobo heaven. Here all the boxcars are empty, handouts grow on bushes, every cop has a wooden leg, and the brakemen (or shacks, as they are called in railroad lingo) tip their hats to the bums.

There are coal-mine folk heroes, too: strong men, brave men, sweet singers—and their songs. Some of the best known coal-mine songs are "The Broken Shovel" that "was broke in two," "The Pretty Maid Milking Her Goat," who would not marry a man if he wore No. 9 boots, and "Down in the Coal Mine," which has been called "the best known mining song in the country." "The Lonely Miner of Wilkes Barre" and "The Avondale Mine Disaster" stand out among many others.

More than one third of the State of Pennsylvania is colored by the rich folklore of the Pennsylvania Dutch (or Pennsylvania Germans). Through nineteen counties and parts of twelve others lie the beautiful Pennsylvania Dutch farms, where real hex signs vie with fake hex signs on the big old barns. (*Hexe* is the German word for witch; and a hex sign is believed to be a protection against witchcraft.) The usual hex sign is a rose cross (the rose superimposed on a cross within a circle). Seven of these on a barn protect cattle and horses and stored grain against malicious witchcraft.

The pretzel is a Pennsylvania Dutch gift to America. Moravian monks at Bethlehem, Pennsylvania, first made the distinctive crisp salty pretzels in the symbolic shape of "seraphim in adoration" with their arms crossed across their breasts.

The *putz* (also Moravian) is another Pennsylvania Dutch contribution to American culture. The putz is a miniature landscape laid out beneath a Christmas tree: a dainty setting of brooks and hills and snow, a tiny town, farm animals, and nowadays a little station and a little train, to signify that Christmas belongs to all places and all ages of the world.

The Easter-egg tree is another Pennsylvania Dutch symbol and can be seen in Pennsylvania Dutch country every spring. It is usually either a birch or a cherry tree. Its trunk and branches are wound with white cotton batting or strips of white cloth, and it is hung with a myriad of colored Easter eggs. The egg, of course, is the world-wide symbol for new life; and it is believed that setting up an Easter-egg tree will bring children to the childless.

Rhode Island

SOME people say that Rhode Island was named *Roodt Eylandt,* red island, by the Dutch navigator Adriaen Block when he first saw the red clay bluffs along its shores; others say it was so called by the Florentine explorer Verrazano because it was "about the bigness of the Island of Rhodes."

> *Nicknames:* Land of Roger Williams, Little Rhody, Plantation State

Rhode Island is called the Land of Roger Williams for the founder of Providence Plantations, as it was first called. It is called Little Rhody because it is the smallest state in the Union. The name Plantation State is a diminutive of its full name: the State of Rhode Island and Providence Plantations.

The people are nicknamed Gunflints because during Dorr's Rebellion in 1842 they fought with the old gunflint type of arms.

Rhode Island has one of the most famous phantom ships of the American coast. In the winter of 1750–1751 the Dutch ship *Palatine* set sail for America with passengers and merchandise, but never reached her destination. Storms blew her off course; a savage crew murdered the captain and proceeded to starve the passengers for their money, making them pay exorbitant sums for a piece of bread or a cup of tea. Then with the money and stores they abandoned ship, leaving the *Palatine* and her passengers to their fate. Unsteered and unmanned, the ship struck Block Island one Sunday morning of Atlantic winter storm.

The people on shore set out to rescue the victims, and when the emaciated, starving survivors were safely off, set fire to the *Palatine,* lest the wreck become a danger to other ships. As the ship burned,

143

a wild, maniac scream was heard above the roar of fire and storm. They had unknowingly overlooked a mad woman who was confined on board. One year after this to the very day, the people of Block Island had to watch the *Palatine* reappear, wreck herself again in the storm, burn with flame and smoke to the water's edge, and hear again the terrible scream of the poor woman who had been left on board. The next year, on the same day, this happened again; and it happened for many, many years thereafter. It occurs less frequently now than it used to.

The folklore of Rhode Island is for the most part, of course, the folklore of New England. The fierce local pride of dwellers in the Narragansett region is the same local pride that burns in every little community dotted across this land between two oceans. Rhode Island tall tales (of the tough fowl which couldn't be carved no matter how long it was cooked; of fish so numerous that people walked dry shod across their backs; of the man who could kick the ceiling with both feet at the same time; and the man who set fire to his haystacks to keep them from blowing away in a windstorm) are found with slight variation everywhere in America, but have been made Rhode Island's own by local ascription of them to actual named persons and places.

South Carolina

STATE FLOWER   *yellow jasmine,* or *Carolina jessamine*

STATE BIRD   *Carolina wren*

SOUTH CAROLINA got its name the same way North Carolina did—from Charles I of England, who named the whole Carolina region for himself. The division into North and South Carolina came in 1665.

> *Nicknames:* Iodine State, Palmetto State, Rice State, Sand-lapper State, Swamp State

South Carolina is called the Iodine State because the food plants grown there are rich in iodine. Palmetto State is the official nickname because of the beautiful palmetto trees which line the coasts. It is called the Rice State (or *was* called the Rice State) because for many years it produced more rice than any other state. And it is called the Sand-lapper State for its vast, barren, sandy regions covered with scrub pine, where the people say they "cain't raise nothin'" and just lap up the sand. It is called the Swamp State for its numerous rice swamps and other swamp regions.

The people are nicknamed Palmettos for their state and are also called Clay-eaters, Sand-lappers, and Weasels. The epithet Clay-eaters was given to the poor white people of certain isolated sections who were known to eat the white clay of the region when they lacked food. The people of the sand ridges were first facetiously called Sand-lappers; now the nickname is apt to be given to any South Carolinian. The most remote backwoods dwellers of South Carolina are referred to as Weasels.

South Carolina has three distinct sections: the coastal plain with its palmettos and beautiful sea islands, the uplands which are becoming more and more industrialized, and the sand and pine barrens where the Sand-lappers live. This is the traditional "poor

146

land"—land so poor that they have to put baking powder in the coffins when they bury people, so the dead can rise on judgment day.

South Carolina is one of the states which comprise the deep South. It has been reported that before the Civil War tar babies were sometimes painted on shop doors, in the belief that the tar baby would catch a thief as surely as it caught Brer Rabbit in the folk tale.

The plat-eye is a very special kind of South Carolina ghost. It first came to South Carolina on a boat from the West Indies. It is always the ghost of someone who has been hurriedly or not properly buried. It may appear to walkers on lonely roads in the light of the new moon in the form of a dog with flickering fiery eyes, or as a headless man, or just as a cloud of white vapor which will surround you and suffocate you. The only thing to do is run.

There is a fragile little lizard common in South Carolina which will shed its tail in your hand in order to escape being held. But South Carolina Negroes say it will come back and get it, and put it on again. The screech owl is called the "death-owl" in South Carolina. Turn your pockets inside out to make one stop hooting.

The beautiful old seaport city of Charleston, famous for its Azalea Festival, still clings to its old ways of Southern life. Old women still walk the streets on certain days crying "Mon———key meat!" Children rush to buy it when they hear the rising note of the monkey-meat cry, but monkey meat turns out to be nothing stranger than molasses candy filled with coconut.

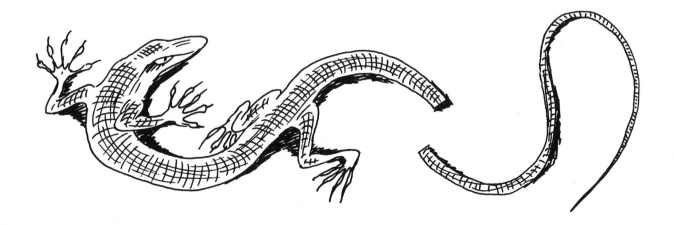

South Dakota

STATE FLOWER   *pasqueflower*

STATE BIRD   *ring-necked pheasant*

SOUTH DAKOTA, like North Dakota, was named for the Dakota Indians who formerly occupied the region. The division into North and South Dakota came in 1889.

Nicknames: Blizzard State, Coyote State

South Dakota is called the Blizzard State because a South Dakota blizzard is about as bad as a blizzard can get, and because the black blizzards (dust storms) of the drought years, which swirl up and carry away hundreds of square miles of top soil, are even more terrible than the white blizzards of winter. It is called the Coyote State (officially) for the great number of coyotes which used to run the plains. The people are sometimes called Coyotes for their state.

South Dakota is all prairie—all, that is, except the Bad Lands with their fantastic eroded rock formations and colors, in the southwestern part of the state, and the Black Hills to the west. There are tales that the Black Hills were piled up by Paul Bunyan over the grave of Babe the Blue Ox, but other people say the Black Hills were there long before then. This state has its own crop of dry-weather jokes and tall tales, its big-wind and cyclone stories, cold-weather and blizzard yarns, its huge-crop lore east of the Missouri River, and its cowboy lore in the ranching regions west of the Missouri. But much South Dakota legend centers around Deadwood in the Black Hills, where Deadwood Dick came searching for gold in 1876.

Deadwood was a gold-boom town, an outlaw town and badman rendezvous. It was there that Wild Bill Hickock was shot in the back one night (August 2, 1876) while he was playing poker

with his back to an open door. Wild Bill was a scout of the Plains, a famous "shootin' peace officer" who killed only in self-defense or in the performance of duty. But he was a bad man to irritate. He had the name of once having killed ten men single-handed; and once he saved the immortal Deadwood stagecoach from five armed horsemen. He died clutching the poker hand he held: a pair of aces and one of eights which ever since has been called the "dead man's hand." They say that his mustache was beautiful even in death.

Calamity Jane, too, won her fame at Deadwood, South Dakota, as pony-express rider and deadshot. She and Wild Bill Hickock are buried side by side.

Tennessee

STATE FLOWER *iris*

STATE BIRD *mockingbird*

TENNESSEE is named for its river, but what the word itself really means is not known. The narrative of the inland expeditions of the Spanish explorer Juan Pardo in 1566–1567 mentions that he came to a Cherokee Indian village named *Tanasqui* on what is now the Little Tennessee River. It is thought this town may have given the river its name, and that it may be the same as the *Tanasi* or *Tanassee* or *Tansi* of other early writers.

Nicknames: Big Bend State, Hog and Hominy State, Volunteer State

Tennessee is called the Big Bend State because the Tennessee River is called the "river with the big bend." In fact some claims have been made that this is the meaning of the Indian word *tanasi* or *tanasee*. It was called the Hog and Hominy State in the first half of the nineteenth century because of its phenomenal production of pork and corn. Volunteer State is the official nickname, because in 1847 when Texas called for volunteers to fight against Mexico for Texan independence, 30,000 Tennessee men stepped forth at once.

The people are sometimes called Big-benders. They were first called Butternuts during the Civil War for the color of their uniforms, but they liked the name and it stuck.

Tennessee folk heroes are John Henry, Davy Crockett, and Sergeant Alvin C. York. John Henry was born in Tennessee. "John Henry told his captain, I am a Tennessee man." These words are in some of the fifty versions of the John Henry ballad. Davy Crockett was also born in Tennessee. He was a member of the Tennessee legislature and left Tennessee to fight for Texas: one of those famous volunteers who gave the Volunteer State its name. Sergeant

Alvin C. York was a Tennessee mountain boy of World War I fame who tricked the Germans with Indian-fighting tricks he had learned in the Tennessee mountains.

In 1946 Dr. E. C. Kirkland made a checklist of the folk songs of Tennessee and came up with 2,442 titles, including the variants. This is not a list of songs known and sung in Tennessee only, but a list of all the songs known and sung in Tennessee. "What Did Tennessee?" is one of them; "Chewin' Chawin' Gum" is another. There are nine versions of the John Henry ballad and thirty-four versions of "Barbara Allen" sung in the state. Almost all the familiar traditional titles are included and many unfamiliar surprising titles, like "The Baldheaded End of the Broom."

In some sections of Tennessee, they say that if you are setting out seedlings or young trees, you have to name them to make sure they will grow.

What do folks call little gray cats in Tennessee? *Kittens!*

Texas

THE State of Texas gets its name from the Hasinai Indians, a confederacy of tribes commonly called *Texas*. The word *texas (texias, teysas)* means friends, or allies. The Hasinai were the first big group of friendly Indians whom the Spanish knew in that region, and they named the region for the people. First the republic and then the state was so named.

Nicknames: Banner State, Beef State, Jumbo State, Lone Star State

Texas has been called the Banner State because it polls such a huge vote in national elections, and it is called the Jumbo State because it is the biggest in the Union. It is called the Beef State because so much of the country's beef is raised on its cattle ranches. The official nickname is Lone Star State for the one star in the state flag. Texans themselves are sometimes called Beef-heads, and they are called Cowboys or Rangers because of the fame of Texas cowboys and Texas Rangers.

Texas is BIG: bigger than Germany, bigger than France. It is as big as New York, Pennsylvania, Massachusetts, Ohio, Illinois, and Wisconsin put together. Everything in it is big, from the hats to the grapefruit. A favorite Texas joke is that nine grapefruit make a dozen. And its weather embraces everything from big winds and big blizzards to tropic sun.

Texas folklore is many things, but most of it stems from four sources: native Indian folklore; Mexican folk tales, beliefs, songs, and legends; Negro tales, jokes, songs, and beliefs; and the folklore of the white settlers. This last consists largely of the lore of the cattle country (with its wealth of cowboy song, belief, cures, and lingo), oil-field lore, weather lore, local legends, bragging tales, and place-name stories. (Whoever drinks of the Nueces River in Texas will never tell the truth again—or want to.)

When anyone brags that Texas is fuller of brimstone than hell, the reference is to the sulfur industry, for Texas produces 85 per cent of all the sulfur used all over the world. The Devil gets his from Texas, too.

Among the big-wind yarns is one about the man who leaned out the train window and lost his hat in the wind; but the wind beat the train to the next station, so he got it back all right from the stationmaster.

The singing cowboy of the movies is not an invention of the motion-picture industry. Many people do not know that part of the cowboy's job was to sing to the cattle. They sang in quick rhythm to hurry up dawdlers behind the herd. They made up and sang the famous night-herding songs to lull the cattle to sleep; and they sang to prevent stampedes.

One of the cowboy's duties was guard duty—riding round and round the big herd all night. As they rode, they sang. "Lay down, little dogies, lay down," says one of the famous lullabies, or night-herding songs. "Oh, say, little dogies, when you goin' to lay down?" "Snore loud, little dogies," is another admonition. The songs in the familiar voice quieted the restless ones and cast fear out of the herd that might otherwise stampede when a wolf howled in the night. Almost all the little dogie songs were made up to prevent stampedes.

A "little dogie" is a young, stunted calf that has been forced to eat grass and go on the trail before it is really able. Consequently they become potbellied from the semi-digested food; and the cowboys called them "dough-guts" because they looked as if they were full of dough. Dough-guts became shortened to "dough-gies," and that is the way the word is pronounced.

The favorite song of the cowboys themselves is the longest: "The Old Chisholm Trail." It has literally hundreds of verses and any one of five or six different tunes is the *Chizzum* tune. Every man who sang it added a verse or two, they say.

153

In the old days, after taking care of the big herds all winter and branding the yearlings at the spring roundup in early May, the cowboys' next big job was driving the herds up the Chisholm Trail from Texas to Kansas to market, or on to the grasslands of Dakota and Montana. The cattle themselves cut the trail and constant travel kept it cut. It was a long drive (it often took several months) and the men "shortened the trail" with song. When they came to the end of the songs they knew, they made up more. They sang of famous stampedes and cowboy heroism ("Utah Carroll" is such a song), of the hardships of trail life, of loneliness, or homesickness, or the death of a comrade, and of the big spree they would have after payday.

But the Texas cowboy repertoire was full of humor, too. "The Lavender Cowboy" tells the story of a young cowhand who wanted to be a hero but feared he would never make it because he had only two hairs on his chest. He used all kinds of hair tonics and finally attained fame by cleaning up a gang of holdup men. "He died with his six-gun asmokin'," but still with only two hairs on his chest.

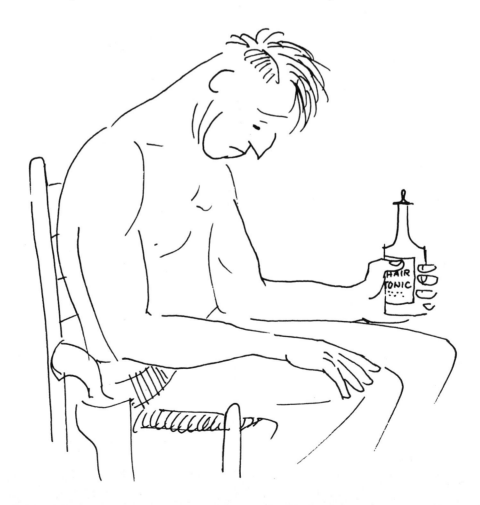

Utah

STATE FLOWER   *sego*

STATE BIRD   *sea gull* (by common consent)

UTAH is the land of the Ute, a large division of North American Indian tribes who formerly inhabited the region, but the meaning of the word *Ute* is not known. There have been many interpretations, some saying that it means "in the tops of the mountains," or "high up," or "on the heights," but modern Americanists have not verified this.

Nicknames: Beehive State, Deseret State, Land of the Saints, Mormon State, Salt Lake State

Utah is called the Beehive State because the beehive is the symbol of industriousness. It is called the Deseret State because that was the first name the Mormon settlers gave to their colony. In the *Book of Mormon,* the word *deseret* means honeybee. It is called the Mormon State or Land of the Saints because it was founded by the Mormons and is still largely populated by Mormons, who refer to themselves as Latter-Day Saints. It is called the Salt Lake State because Great Salt Lake is in Utah. People who live in Utah are

155

apt to be called either Mormons or Saints, whether they are or not.

Utah has a wealth of mining lore. There are tales of the discouraged miner who threw away his pick in despair and discovered silver where it jabbed into the earth, and of the young teamster whose mule kicked up a piece of gold-bearing rock. Utah miners say that wherever the "lead flower" grows, lead ore lies below. The lead flower is the sego lily, state flower of Utah.

But Utah lore is more especially the lore of the Mormons, who founded the state and color its culture. The most famous of the Mormon legends are the legends of the sego lily and the gulls. During the early years of settlement (1847–1851) plagues of black crickets descended on the Mormon farms out of the hills and ate the new-growing grain. The earth was left bare, and the people had no food until the Paiute Indians told them about a nutritious bulb, which they called *sego,* which was plentiful in Utah. The settlers learned to eat it in this time of starvation and were saved.

The story of the gulls is the same story. In May, 1848, millions of black crickets swooped down on the Mormon crops. The people dug holes and buried them by the bushels; they tried to drown them in the irrigation ditches; they tried to stop them with fire. But nothing stopped them. Every day more crickets than ever appeared and continued to eat—and eat—and eat—grain, grass, everything. This meant no grain, no vegetables, no fruit for the settlers, no grass for the cattle, no beef, no milk. Starvation was not far off.

Then suddenly one day the people heard the sound of wings and shrill cries in the air. Thousands of sea gulls came over Great Salt Lake and began to devour the crickets. This happened day after day, and day after day more gulls kept coming. The crickets were annihilated, and the crops and the people survived.

The gull is protected by law in Utah (and no wonder), and was chosen with love and gratitude to be the state bird. And there is a sea-gull monument in Temple Square in Salt Lake City; it depicts two gilded sea gulls alighting on a ball which tops a fifteen-foot granite shaft. At the base of the shaft is a pool where birds habitually drink and splash. Four bronze tablets tell the story of the gulls.

Vermont

STATE FLOWER *red clover*

STATE BIRD *hermit thrush*

THE date of the naming of Vermont is in question, but probably the first to call it for its green hills was Samuel de Champlain, who had seen evergreen-clad hills to the east from Lake Champlain in 1609, which he wrote of as *Verd Mont*.

Nickname: Green Mountain State

157

Vermont is forests and farms, maple sugar, marble, and granite. And it is often said that the population counts more cows than people. Vermont is New England, too—only more so. The Vermont Yankee is the Yankee's Yankee. New Englanders have the reputation of being rugged, taciturn, and austere. Vermonters are more rugged, more silent, and more stern. New Englanders are suspicious of strangers; Vermonters won't even answer, "Yes, it *is* a fine day," unless they know your grandfather. New England humor is wry; Vermont humor is grim.

Vermont was the first state to ban slavery and the last state to abandon the debtors' prison. You can still be put in jail in Vermont for some kinds of debts. Vermont is a strange combination of modern technology and the old simple ways of life—a land of Diesel-powered ski tows and advanced quarrying techniques and kerosene lamps and wood-burning stoves.

Near Cavendish, Vermont, some time ago two young men went together to a rocky place over the Black River to pry out some blocks of rock which they needed for a foundation wall. The spot bordered an eighty-foot precipice over the gorge of the river which swirled with white rapids below. They worked diligently and silently and one of them forgot entirely that they were working on the edge of such a perilous place. When his crowbar slipped, he slipped too, lost his footing, and went hurtling over the edge.

His companion knew that his friend could never survive an eighty-foot fall onto the jagged rocks in the whirlpool. After a few minutes went by, he mustered up enough courage to look over the cliff. He was amazed to see his friend slowly climbing back up!

The young man had fallen through the branches of a tree and grabbed hold. Then he had managed to get his feet onto a ledge, and was climbing inch by inch to the top, by crevice and jutment, up the face of the rock.

"Are you hurt?" yelled his companion.

"Ain't hurt much," said the other sadly, "but I lost my jackknife."

Virginia

STATE FLOWER *dogwood*

STATE BIRD *cardinal*

VIRGINIA was named about 1584 by Queen Elizabeth I of England for herself: the Virgin Queen.

Nicknames: Ancient Dominion, or Old Dominion; Cavalier State; Mother of Presidents

Virginia got the nicknames Ancient Dominion and Old Dominion about 1663 when King Charles II of England added the arms of Virginia to his own royal shield, thus making it a fifth dominion (the other four: England, Scotland, France, Ireland). It was called the Cavalier State because it was settled by English Cavaliers in the time of Charles I, and it is called the Mother of Presidents because it has produced more presidents than any other one state; eight presidents of the United States have been Virginians.

Virginians are called Beadles sometimes because the early courts of Virginia followed the English custom of using beadles (criers or messengers of the court). They are often called Cavaliers in memory of the founders. Virginians are also nicknamed Tuckahoes because (like the people of North Carolina) they, too, learned to eat tuckahoe, or Indian bread, in times of hardship.

Virginia *is* the South—the hospitable South where there is always room for one more in the smallest house or at the poorest table, and where the people don't keer how they talk as long as they don't sound like damyankees.

The Virginia Negro version of the world-wide folk tale about why dogs chase cats says that once Dog had Cat for a wife, but every night when he came home Cat said she was too sick to get supper. This happened all the time. Dog got pretty tired of it.

So one day Dog decided to stay home and hide and watch Cat from the corner of the house. As soon as Cat thought he was gone, she started playing and frisking with the kitten. She wasn't sick at all.

Then Dog came round the house, and Cat quick put a marble in her mouth and said she had a toothache. Dog was so mad he started chasing her, and dogs have been chasing cats ever since.

Washington

STATE FLOWER *rhododendron*

STATE BIRD *willow goldfinch*

THE territory of Washington was named for George Washington in 1853, and the state, of course, retained the name. The state seal bears a bust vignette of the General, enclosed in a circle.

Nicknames: Chinook State, Evergreen State

The State of Washington is often called the Chinook State for the great number of Chinook Indians who formerly occupied the region. It is called the Evergreen State for its forests of Douglas fir and hemlock, and because roses bloom for Christmas. The people are nicknamed Clam-grabbers because they eat quantities of the clams which are so plentiful in Puget Sound.

The folklore of Washington is mostly logging lore and Paul Bunyan stories. (Paul Bunyan dug Puget Sound, for instance.) It is the lore of the old frontier days when there were plenty of stalwart men and no women, and a Mr. Asa Mercer went east and brought back eleven "agreeable young girls" to marry the big, lonely Washington frontiersmen. The girls liked their husbands better in their colorful pioneer garb, the story goes, than they did in the stiff

collars and store suits in which they slicked up for the first intro-
duction. The success of this venture was so genuine that Mr.
Mercer went east again and returned with forty-six widows. And
who ever heard of a Washington old maid to this day?

The unmistakable mark of a Washingtonian, they say, is being
able to reel off Indian names. So if someone says *Smelegamax* or
Upper Utamqt Valley or *snikiepupsa* without batting an eye, your man
is from Washington.

The Okanagon Indians, who formerly occupied the region from
the Columbia River to British Columbia, had several tales explaining the origin of the Columbia River. One of them tells how Coyote
was walking along one hot day and began to feel dry and thirsty.

"I wish there was a cloud," he said.

In a minute along came a cloud and made shade for him.

"Not enough!" said Coyote. "I want more clouds."

Soon the whole sky was dark and lowering. But Coyote still felt hot.

"I wish it would rain," he said.

In a minute there was a sprinkling shower. "Not enough!" said Coyote. "I want more rain."

It began to pour. But still Coyote was not satisfied. "I wish there was a creek," he said, "to cool my feet."

Suddenly a creek ran beside him, and Coyote walked in it.

"Not enough," he said. "Not deep enough!"

Suddenly a big rushing river swirled around him and swept him away, and Coyote was nearly drowned. At last the river washed him up on the bank in a far place and left him there. When he came to, the crows and the ravens and the buzzards were all standing around, wondering if Coyote was drowned and dead.

"I'm not!" said Coyote, and they flew away.

And this was the origin of the great Columbia River.

West Virginia

STATE FLOWER   *rhododendron*

STATE BIRD   *cardinal*

WEST VIRGINIA was so named in 1862, one year after the western section of the huge tract called Virginia became a separate political entity.

Nicknames: Mountain State, Panhandle State

West Virginia is called the Mountain State because it is one of the most mountainous states in the Union, and one third of it is high Allegheny plateau. They had to dig and haul away four mountains in order to build the airport at Charleston. It is called the Panhandle State because on the map it is shaped like a pan with a handle.

West Virginia folklore is hill-country folklore. West Virginia is the country where the hills are so steep and the valleys so narrow that the dogs wag their tails up and down instead of sideways. It is the land where the farmers lean ladders on the hillside in order to get from one field to another—the land where the thin, tall, razor-back hog first developed in his struggle to adapt to the environment. Deadpan farmers tell strangers about the West Virginia cattle with legs shorter on one side than the other, bred that way a-purpose so they can graze on the hills.

And some of the mountain streams are so narrow, they say, that the sunfish and bass can't turn around in them. They have to go up or downstream till they come to some mill with an overshot water wheel, and ride the wheel in order to change directions.

West Virginia is also the state where John Henry beat the steam drill in the Big Bend Tunnel—and died of it, and where John Brown was hanged at Charles Town after his last abolitionist raid. Tony Beaver is the great lumberjack hero of West Virginia, and is often referred to as the Paul Bunyan of West Virginia because many episodes in the Paul Bunyan saga have accrued to his name.

What was the greatest feat of strength ever performed in this country? *Wheeling West Virginia.*

Wisconsin

STATE FLOWER *wood violet*

STATE BIRD *robin*

THE State of Wisconsin is named for the Wisconsin River, which was named by the Menominee Indians for its teeming population of muskrats. The Menominee word for muskrat is written *wi'skos* or *wis'ko^{n}s*. And a certain group of Menominee Indians themselves (who lived where the Wisconsin River and the Mississippi join) were called *Wi'skos Se'peo Wini'niwûk*, Wisconsin River People.

Nickname: Badger State

164

Wisconsin is nicknamed the Badger State in honor of the hardy lead miners who first came into the lead-mine region one spring, years ago, and instead of running home when bitter winter weather arrived, dug into the hills and holed up for the winter, like badgers. The people of Wisconsin are still called Badgers to this day.

Wisconsin folklore, like the folklore of all the states, is many things. Much of it is Indian folklore, for the Indians outnumbered the white man in northern Wisconsin ten to one as late as 1870. The Chippewa hated the white man for only one thing—for laying low the forests—because to them a tree symbolized everything good in the world: health, purity, manhood, and life itself. Much of Wisconsin folklore is German folklore, because (like Pennsylvania) Wisconsin was settled by large numbers of Germans. Wisconsin lore, of course, is also mining lore and logging lore. Paul Bunyan's famous breaking of the jam took place on the Wisconsin River.

Somewhere in northwestern Wisconsin the famous contest between the big spotted steers and the little brown bulls took place. This is the subject of one of America's favorite native ballads—"The Little Brown Bulls." A man named McCluskey owned the big spotted steers, "girt eight foot and three"; and he bet they could skid more logs than Bull Gordon's little brown bulls, they being "girt six foot and nine . . . too light for our pine," he said. He bet twenty-five dollars that the spotted steers could beat "the short-legged and soggy little brown bulls." His steers would skid two to one, he bet!

Everyone knows the end of the story. The ballad gives no details of the actual performance, which must have been a sight to see; but the contest ended with the spotted steers "behind just one mile," with a record of "a hundred and ten and no more," and the little brown bulls beat them "by ten and a score."

Wyoming

STATE FLOWER   *Indian paintbrush*

STATE BIRD   *western meadowlark*

WYOMING was so named when it was first organized into a territory. No one knows exactly why; but it has been assumed that some settler from the Wyoming valley in Pennsylvania must have proposed it. The word itself is from a Delaware Indian word *m'cheuwo'mink*, which means "upon the great plain."

Nicknames: Equality State, Sagebrush State

Wyoming is nicknamed the Equality State because it was the first state in the Union to give equal rights to women (1869). And it is called the Sagebrush State for the wild sage which covers its desert sections.

166

Wyoming, the mile-high state, was the end of the trail for numberless little dogies, driven up the Chisholm Trail from Texas to the high grassland plains where (the cowboys promised them) they would be "beef steers by and by." The refrain of the famous "Whoopee ti yi yo" song says

> Whoopee ti yi yo, git along, little dogies
> For you know Wyoming will be your new home.

Wyoming is still a state of great open spaces, the last stronghold of the old-time cowboy. Here the cowboy life of song and story still goes on, though on a smaller scale. The Powder River, famous for being a mile wide and an inch deep, runs through the Wyoming cattle country. "Let'er buck," they say. "Let'er buck!" (*Let'er buck* is a cattle-country exclamation used either in encouragement or derision.)

Wyoming lore is a conglomeration of cowboy lore, sheepherding lore, oil-boom lore, tales and legends of the Oregon Trail, and of the mountain men.

The mountain men were roving trappers and fur traders of the Rockies who came in from the wilds once a year to some appointed place for a great get-together called the rendezvous. The original purpose of the annual rendezvous was to receive essential supplies sent up from St. Louis, but it always turned into a great rough celebration for the solitary trappers whose one contact with the outside world it was.

The roll call of the mountain men included many famous names. Among them was a certain John Colter, a trapper in the Wyoming mountains, who returned to St. Louis in 1810 with stories of canyons and geysers that got a big laugh everywhere. "Colter's Hell" listeners called the fabulous Yellowstone region which Colter described, and nobody believed a word of it until other fur traders went and saw for themselves.

BAD MEN

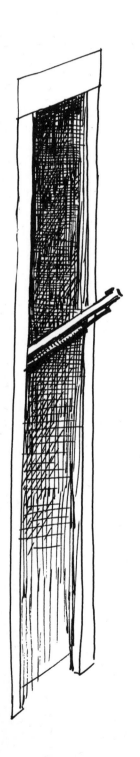

Billy the Kid

BILLY THE KID was the most famous desperado of the Southwest, a supergunman with a sure and deadly aim. He shot two men once with his hands in his pockets. He could toss a hat twenty feet into the air and shoot six holes in it before it hit the ground.

Movies and the comics often make a "good bad man" of him, a kind of Robin Hood hero on the side of right and the common people. Legend also makes a "bad bad man" of him, exaggerates his killings, and pictures him worse than he was. He was handsome, generous, laughing, and brave; or—he was cruel, sullen, heartless, and nerveless.

Billy the Kid's name was William H. Bonney. He was born in New York in 1859, moved with his parents to Kansas, and shot his first man in New Mexico at the age of twelve for insulting his mother. He killed twenty-one men in twenty-one years, a figure which debunkers have debunked down to seven—sometimes to three.

Eventually, Billy the Kid was hired by two ruthless cattle kings, Old John Chisum and Alex McSwain. These men had built a monopoly of the stock-grazing business, which they kept at the point of a gun. They turned 80,000 cattle into the territory, and the little herds of little owners were swept into the greater one, sometimes by chance but always by intent. And when the little ranchmen went out in search of their own, there was deadly conflict. This conflict, known as the Lincoln County war, was also called the War of Billy the Kid. Chisum and McSwain hired Billy the Kid as one of their number: Billy the Kid, daredevil rider, sure shot, and lighthearted killer—hired for these reasons.

One day Billy was sent out to bring in two herders who were suspected of working against Chisum, and on the way back he shot them both for trying to escape. Then he shot his closest friend and companion, McClusky, because he objected to the shooting of two defenseless herders.

This was the day—a Monday—when things began to catch up with Billy the Kid. Three murders in one afternoon were bound to leak out, and they did.

Dead men don't talk, but their friends do. News of the three murders reached the Lincoln County authorities on Wednesday.

Sheriff Brady decided to go after the Kid at once, before the Kid could be forewarned.

So, on Thursday morning, June 13, 1879, Sheriff Brady and his deputy, George Hindman, set out for Chisum's ranch where they knew Billy the Kid was hiding. Both of them realized they might never come back alive. Brady was hoping that they could take the Kid by surprise and capture him without blood and battle, but neither Brady nor Hindman really believed this would happen.

Those who were around the Kid that Thursday said he was restless and alert every minute. He had a hunch that "something will happen today." At nine in the morning he cleaned his rifle and loaded it, and got ready his derringers (short-barreled pistols). At eleven o'clock he saw two horsemen on the horizon, five miles away, approaching from the west. Twenty minutes later he looked at them again through a spyglass. "Sheriff," he said, and walked out of the house. He walked to the edge of the little settlement into McSwain's house to await the officers. In another twenty minutes they had arrived.

Then Billy the Kid stepped outside the door. He raised his rifle and aimed at Brady's heart. Bang! Then another bang. When the smoke cleared, Sheriff Brady was dead and Hindman was dying.

173

In the next half hour the Kid gathered together a group of comrades, sixty-five men willing to follow him into the mountains. They were well equipped with horses, guns, and ammunition. Thus Billy the Kid became an outlaw and prepared to defend himself against authority.

The next two years were a series of bloody fights and thrilling getaways. Numerous posses headed by the law attacked Billy the Kid and his outlaws. Many were killed, but the Kid was never taken. He led a charmed life. No one could touch him.

One moonlight night in July, 1881, Billy the Kid slipped into a little shack behind the house of Pete Maxwell in the town of Fort Sumner, New Mexico. Fort Sumner was his headquarters those days; he made a living round about, gambling and stealing cattle. The little shack belonged to a Mexican who worked for Pete Maxwell and who idolized the Kid. Some say she was a beautiful young half-breed, the sweetheart of the Kid; some say she was a fat, motherly old Mexican woman. Either way, the shack was always a haven for Billy the Kid.

This night the Kid was hungry. But there was no meat in the shack. He picked up a slicing knife and was going to cut a piece from the supply in Pete Maxwell's kitchen. Pete Maxwell had always seemed friendly enough.

As he silently passed by the end of the porch in the moonlight, he was seen by Sheriff Pat Garrett and his deputy, who had been tipped off that the Kid would "be around" that night. They were waiting for him.

"Who's that?" they said. They thought it was the servant.

"Who's that?" said Billy the Kid quickly, and he backed into the dark house.

"That's him!" said Pete Maxwell to the sheriff. And Sheriff Pat Garrett fired.

When they cautiously approached the open door, there lay Billy the Kid in a streak of moonlight, barefoot, with a Colt 41 in one hand and a meat knife in the other.

Railroad Bill

MORRIS SLATER was a big, dark-brown Alabama Negro bad man. He was called Railroad Bill because he hopped freight trains to make his getaways and robbed freight trains to make a living. He used to break a seal on a freight car and climb in. Then when the train was going a pretty clip through some wooded place he would throw out the stuff—canned goods and hardware, but especially canned foods—and then hop off and walk back along the track and pick it up.

This way he had plenty to eat, and what was left over he'd sell to backwoods people, lots cheaper than the stores could sell the same thing. This made the white storekeepers awful mad, and they all had it in for him.

It all started one day when Morris Slater walked into town carrying his hunting rifle loosely under one arm. This was against the law in those days (1893), and a policeman demanded that he give it up. Slater refused to give it up. The policeman tried to take it away, so Slater shot him and ran.

A freight train happened to be racketing past the town at the moment, so Slater hopped it to get away. Bands of men hunted for him all through the area, but they never found him. It was after this first escape that people began to call him Railroad Bill.

Slater rode the freight until he came to a thickly wooded region far from town. Then he jumped off and lit into the woods. He found an old voodoo man back there and lived with him a long time. He would help the old fellow—get his firewood or go hunting and bring home meat—and in return the old man taught him some of his voodoo secrets and powers.

After that it seemed as if Railroad Bill had luck with everything, robbing stores and trains. He always got his man and no man ever got him. Year after year the posses hunted him, sometimes with dogs, but never caught him.

He knew how to change himself into a sheep or a bullock. Then he'd just stand in the field, looking stupid, and watch the posse ride by. But inside he was laughing. Once a posse riding with dogs raised a little red fox and it ran ahead of them, laughing. Sometimes a ribby little short-haired, dark-brown dog would be seen among the bloodhounds hunting for Railroad Bill. Then it wouldn't be long before the hounds would lose the scent or take up a wrong one. And the little dog would suddenly not be there. No one ever quite saw where he ran off to. Into the woods—somewhere.

Railroad Bill was always welcome in the little shacks in the woods. The people welcomed him with his loot which he sold so cheap. When they learned he was a hunted man, they hid and protected him and would have welcomed him without the loot. They gloried in his luck and in his powers to escape. Just to know him or harbor him was to partake of that luck, somehow. It bucked them up. Just to touch him brought luck. They believed in it completely.

Of course there was a price on his head: $1,250 for Railroad Bill. And of course he was caught at last. Two men, R. C. John and Leonard McGowan, shot him down in a country store in broad daylight one day in March, 1896, and got the reward. But the people in the woods never believed that Railroad Bill was dead. They heard the news from time to time, but they never believed it.

"Railroad Bill! Dead? Not him!"

Jesse James

JESSE JAMES was a bad man, the most famous bad man and perhaps the most beloved bad man of them all; bandit, bank robber, train robber, murderer, outlaw, desperado. He was born in Clay County, Missouri, in 1847 and did his first serious shooting at the age of fifteen, when he joined up with William C. Quantrill's Confederate guerrillas.

By the time Jesse James was nineteen, he and his older brother Frank were leaders of a band of fearless young robbers and killers, who robbed banks and held up trains and killed whoever got in the way, all over the central states.

He was *the* good bad man of all good bad men who stole from the rich to give to the poor. All the Jesse James ballads and legends say so. One of the best-known stories of Jesse's tender heart is the one about the widow's mortgage.

One day somewhere in Missouri the two James boys and their gang were riding along on horseback. By noon they were hungry, so they stopped at a small farmhouse and asked for something to eat. The woman hadn't much in the house, she said, but she would

make them a lunch from whatever she had. While the boys sat
around the room waiting, Jesse noticed that tears were streaming
down the woman's face. He asked what was the matter, and finally
got the whole story. The mortgage was due on the little farm—that
very day, that very afternoon the man was coming—and she hadn't
even a dollar; her husband was dead; she had three small children.
The man who held the mortgage was a hardhearted man and
would surely put her and her children off the place.

"How much is the mortgage?" asked Jesse.

"$1,500—" but why ask? She had no money; she could not pay
even part of it.

"Here!" said Jesse, counting money out of a little bag onto the
table. "Here. Here's $1,500. You pay off that mortgage."

The woman was speechless. She couldn't take all that, she protested; she could never pay it back. But Jesse kept saying not to worry about that, just to pay off that mortgage.

"But *get a receipt!*" he warned. "Make the man sign a receipt *in ink.*"

The young widow promised faithfully that she would do so.

"What does that fellow look like, anyway?" asked Jesse. So the woman described the hardhearted miser, even down to the color of his horse.

Jesse and the boys said good-by then and started on their way. But they did not go far. They hid in the woods, waiting for the man to go by, and they kept on waiting until he came back again, looking smug and triumphant over the wad in his pocket. Then they just stepped into the road and took it away from him.

The story of Anne Limrick's watch is a similar tale. William Limrick was president of the bank in Lexington, Missouri, when it was held up and looted by Jesse James and his gang. Among the things stolen was a beautiful enameled watch which Mr. Limrick had bought as a gift for his young daughter Anne.

In a matter of seconds one day five young horsemen had appeared, entered the bank, tied up the employees, taken everything, and left just as suddenly as they had appeared. It was Jesse James and his gang; people in the street had recognized them. But they were never caught.

One day months later Anne Limrick received a small package

from New York from an unknown sender. She opened it and could hardly believe her eyes—for there was the precious watch. Jesse James had seen the young girl's name engraved on the back and had returned it to her.

One day in 1876 the gang held up a bank in Northfield, Minnesota, and had no luck. Several of them were killed, and Jesse and Frank just escaped with their lives. So they decided to lie low for a while. They did nothing conspicuous for three years, and then one Wednesday night, "it was bright moonlight," Jesse and Frank stopped and robbed the Glendale train.

This was the beginning of the end. Their victims had recognized them, and the law could take no more. The governor of Missouri put a price of $10,000 on Jesse's head, dead or alive. He was then living in St. Joseph, Missouri, and one night he was caught off guard in his own home by an old friend, Robert Ford, who shot him through the head—for the money.

> It was one of the gang called little Robert Ford
> Who shot Jesse James on the sly.

This happened on a Saturday night, April 2, 1882. Jesse's wife and three young children were in the adjoining room.

> It was Robert Ford, that dirty coward,
> I wonder how he does feel.
> He ate Jesse's bread and slept in Jesse's bed
> And he put Jesse James in his grave.

This sounds like the end of the story—and it is—except that people are unwilling to relinquish their heroes. Rumors and declarations that Jesse James was still alive kept cropping up for years. Seventeen fake Jesse Jameses have claimed to be the original. The last one was an old man, 100 years old, known as Frank Dalton, whose claim to being Jesse James filled American newspapers during May and June of 1948. But the possibility of his father's survival was denied by Jesse James, Jr., who vividly remembered what happened in the next room that Saturday night in 1882.

The immortality of Jesse James lies in his legend.

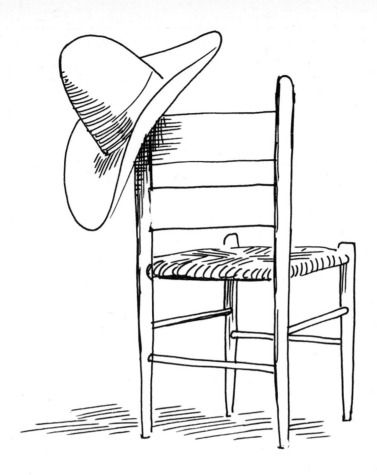

Stackalee

STACKALEE was a big Negro bad man born on Market Street in St. Louis in 1861. He was born double-jointed and with a full set of teeth and red eyes. "A gipsy told his mother, Told her like a friend, Your double-jointed baby, Won't come to no good end." So says one of the legends which celebrate his name.

Stackalee was named for the famous boat he worked on. He was a stoker or roustabout on the Mississippi-Ohio River packet, *Stacker Lee,* which plied between Memphis, Cincinnati, St. Louis, and Vicksburg. People spell his name Stagolee sometimes, but mostly they call him Stack.

Stack was a fine musician. He could play the guitar and the piano, and he was always moaning the blues or beating out some

181

rag. Women loved him. When he hugged the girls he squeezed the breath out of them, and they liked that.

Stack's own girl was born on Market Street in St. Louis in 1861, just like Stack himself. Her name was Stack o' Dollars. They called her that because she not only *had* a stack of dollars but always bet them all in a gambling game. She was a big fat girl with diamond teeth and *some smile*. She smoked cigars and could lick any man in town in a fist fight. Stack did like a spirited woman. She wore a Stetson hat, too—a bigger one than Stack's.

Stack always wore a Stetson hat, the five-gallon size. He dearly loved a Stetson, and had a whole row of them, all different colors, hanging on pegs in the house on Market Street. Everybody says he sold his soul to the Devil in return for a magic spell on his favorite Stetson. He could get away with anything as long as he wore that hat. And he was never caught as long as he had it.

Stackalee was a gambler, a gunman, and a killer. Nobody knows how many notches he had on his gun for the men he had killed. He feared no one. He even challenged Jesse James once, but that was a mistake. Nobody was a match for Jesse James in *any* kind of fight, and the minute Jesse let go of him Stack beat it for the mountains.

Once in the mountains he met up with two deputies who were out looking for him in order to collect the $5,000 reward on his head. So he sat down to chat with them and pass the time of day. Stack learned their names and then shot their initials in their hats before they discovered who he was. He nearly split his sides laughing to see how fast they left the neighborhood.

But every bad man gets caught up with, one way or another, it seems, and the Devil was getting tired of Stack's devilment. He was tired of waiting to snatch Stack's soul to hell, too.

Stack was in a gambling game one night in St. Louis. He was winning, seemed as if he couldn't lose, and he was so busy scraping in the money that he forgot about his hat which he had hung on the back of his chair. This was the Devil's chance. In the guise of a nice young man named Billy Lyons he took the hat and headed for a barrel house down the street, where he knew Billy Lyons to be. With a yell in his throat and a gun in each hand Stack tore after him. When he got there, there was Billy Lyons all right, smoking a cigarette, easylike, expecting nothing; but the Stetson hat was not in sight.

Stack shot him on sight and killed him dead for stealing the magic Stetson that had always saved him from the law. Onlookers said Billy had not left the barrel house all evening, but Stack did not believe that.

The police wagon came and hauled Stackalee off to jail. But the Devil got cheated out of Stack's soul, after all, for they did not hang him. The judge sentenced him to a stretch of seventy-five years in Jefferson penitentiary, and there he is. He has served thirty-four years and has forty-one still to go. So the Devil is still waiting.

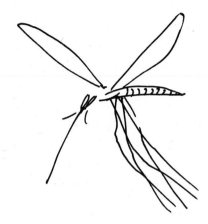

TALL TALK

Spring Flood

PROBABLY one of the most famous tall yarns in America is a flood story. Spring freshets often flood the meadows of American hill country and sometimes rise as high as the second floor of near-by farmhouses. One spring the waters came and spread around the farmhouse of a certain young farmer and his wife who lived on the bank of a New England river, and continued to rise until the first floor was submerged. The neighbors were worried about the predicament of their friends and decided to go after them in a boat.

They rowed in the front door and finally found the pair upstairs, sitting on a bed. The farmer and his wife were delighted to be rescued; they were glad to get into the boat and be rowed to some higher and drier place. But just as they were leaving, the young farmer thought a drink of cider all round would be a fitting token of gratitude for such friendship and concern. So he jumped out of the boat, ran down cellar, got the cider, and treated the crowd. As soon as everybody had enough, the rescue party resumed its oars and the young farmer and his wife were safely conducted to dry land.

Icebergs

ONCE there was a man who had snow scenes and icebergs painted on his bedroom wall during a hot spell. The water froze in the water pitcher the first night, and he had to build a fire the second and write off to Sears, Roebuck for five blankets.

The Talking-match

KENTUCKIANS tell one about a talking-match between a Frenchman and a man from Kentucky. Each bet five dollars that he could outtalk the other. Well, they talked for thirteen hours, and then the judges and listeners-in fell asleep. In the morning the Frenchman was dead, and the man from Kentucky was kneeling beside him, whispering into his ear.

They Just Go Round

THEN there's that crooked stream down on the farm: so crooked that anyone who tries to jump across it lands on the same side every time! People don't try it any more. They just go round.

Mosquitoes

ALMOST every state in the Union has bigger mosquitoes than any other state in the Union. In Mississippi four of them can hold a man down. In Florida they are so ferocious that the people have to sleep with their heads in iron kettles, and even then they can't sleep because of the noise the creatures make drilling through the iron with their stingers. In New Jersey they have hit on a way to put a stop to this kind of thing by riveting the stinger just as it comes through. People from New York say that Texas mosquitoes are as big as pelicans and just as hungry; Texans, however, say that they never get bigger than mockingbirds.

Callin' the Dog

WHEN a bunch of people get together in Mississippi just for the fun of some tall talk, they call it "calling the dog." This term comes from a famous tall-tale session at which one man said he'd give a hound pup to the one that told the biggest lie. Well, everybody stretched his tongue that night. Each tale in turn was a whopper that seemed to top the last. Finally it was the last man's turn. He had no tale to tell, he said. "I never told a lie in my life," he said. *You get the dog!* said the owner of the pup, and the vote was unanimous.

The shaggy dog story is just the opposite of tall talk. It is a long, drawn-out tale finally reaching an anticlimax behind a smoke screen of detail, the same detail repeated again and again. The genre was named from the so-called "original" which centered around a shaggy dog.

The Shaggy Dog

A WOMAN had a big shaggy dog of which she was very fond. She took it to England with her and on the way home, somewhere between Southampton and Schenectady, New York, it got lost. So she advertised, describing her pet in detail.

> Lost: big shaggy dog; big reward; all expenses of finder will be paid to bring it to this address.

Soon thereafter people began to come with shaggy dogs. Day after day the bell would ring, and there would stand someone with a shaggy dog. But always the dog was not shaggy enough. Often the dog answered the description in the ad—*almost*. The woman would say "Yes. He looks a lot like my dog, but my dog was shaggier than that." This went on for months, but none of the finds were quite shaggy enough. The woman kept the ad in the paper and even advertised in several papers in England.

One day she received a letter from England. A man there had seen her ad and had found a dog that answered the description so closely that he was sure this must be her shaggy dog. The woman thought so too. So she sent the fare for the man and dog to come to the United States and sent extra fare for him to get from New York to Schenectady.

The big day came. The doorbell rang. The woman opened the door and looked at the dog, and said,

"Oh! Not THAT shaggy!"

STRANGE

TALES

The Ghostly Hitchhiker

ONCE there was a university sophomore who went to a fraternity dance. There he met the most beautiful girl he had ever seen in his life. He fell in love at once, and they danced together several times, but the girl did not say much. Suddenly, while they were dancing, she said, "Will you take me home?"

"Of course, if you wish," he answered.

So they left the room, and the boy drove the girl home in his roadster. She gave him the address and told him how to get there, but that was the end of the conversation.

Once she said, "Oh, I'm so cold!" The boy then stopped the car, took off his coat, and put it around her.

When they arrived at the house and the girl was about to go in, the boy said, "What is your name?"

"Mamie," she said, and she turned and waved to him as she disappeared in the door.

The next day the boy drove out to the house again to see Mamie. He knocked on the door, and a bent old woman opened it.

"I have come to see Mamie," he said.

195

"You have come to see Mamie," said the old woman softly, puzzled.

"Yes." And the boy explained that he had met her at the college dance, driven her home, and lent her his coat.

"Come in," said the old woman. And there was a photograph of the beautiful girl on the parlor mantel.

"May I see Mamie?" the boy asked.

The old woman pointed to the picture. "Yes, that's Mamie," he said, "but may I see her now?"

"Mamie was my daughter," the old woman said. "She has been dead for five years."

"But I danced with her last night!" the boy said. "I brought her home."

"Mamie has been dead for five years," the old woman said again, quietly.

"How can that be?" said the boy. "We danced together last night! She borrowed my coat!"

The old woman repeated that Mamie was dead, and if the young man did not believe her, he could go look at Mamie's stone in the graveyard. So the boy went. He walked through the graveyard paths and finally saw his coat hanging on a small stone not far ahead. He picked up the coat and read:

MAMIE
Beloved daughter of

———————————

The ghostly hitchhiker has thumbed a ride in every one of the United States. It is probably the best-known and most popular

ghost story in America. In the horse-and-buggy days our grand-fathers used to meet her in her party dress—a young girl—late at night on some dark country road. The above version of the story turns up around every college and university and in every little college town, wherever boys go to dances and drive convertibles. In the Yale version the coat on the little gravestone is a Yale blazer. Yale students say, "But this is a *true story*—not a folk tale! It happens all the time!" It has happened so often in New Haven that now the boys recognize the girl and don't stop to pick her up.

One of the most familiar versions of the story is told of a New York doctor who was driving home very late one night from the city to a Connecticut suburb. As he slowed up for a certain highway intersection noted for its many accidents, he saw a young girl in an evening dress by the side of the road, signaling for him to stop. He jammed on his brakes, and the girl said, "Please, please take me home." He consented, of course, and the girl climbed into the back seat and gave him an address in a town not far away.

"What are you doing here all alone at this hour?"

"Oh, it's too long a story! I'll tell you later. Just *please* take me home."

So the doctor started the car and drove quickly to the address. But when he stopped in front of the house to let the girl out, there was no girl in the back seat. He was completely astonished; he did not know what to think. He decided, however, that he had better let the family know what had happened, so he rang the bell.

A sad-looking man finally came to the door and asked what was wanted. The doctor told his story: at a certain intersection he had picked up a lovely girl who had asked to be brought to this address, and—

"Yes," said the man. "That was my daughter. She was killed in an accident at that intersection five years ago."

In New Orleans a young girl dressed in white stands at the entrance to a cemetery and signals taxis. She always asks the driver to ring the bell at the address to which she is driven. The man who answers the door says the young girl is his wife who died on their bridal night. When they open the door of the cab, of course, the girl is gone.

Dr. Louis C. Jones turned up forty-nine versions of this tale for the State of New York alone in the New York State College Folklore Archives. The hitchhiker is always a girl, thinly clad, or a young woman; in one version she is a nun. Time after time the story says the girl was killed in an automobile accident. The address is always correct; the girl did live there—once.

The Big Black Umbrella

"DEATH got no friends." This is an old saying of South Carolina Negroes. Everybody knows that the living forget the dead. But everybody does *not* know that the dead never forget the dead. Every year in the spring, about Easter, they say, the dead hold a remembrance service for the sad forgotten dead.

The big black umbrella stood in the corner of Mary Simmons' room. When it rained she used it, and it kept her dry. But nobody ever borrowed it. No one would think of asking to borrow it. If anyone had, Mary would have refused. It was not for lending.

Mary Simmons was a Negro cook and washerwoman in Charleston, South Carolina, and she lived in a small house in a forgotten old neighborhood bordering a forgotten old burying ground for the poor. On Sunday afternoons Mary liked to sit by her window and take a cat nap.

One drizzly Sunday afternoon she was wakened from one of these cat naps by the sound of singing. What was the song? It

seemed to be coming from the near-by burying ground. What were they singing?

> No more rain gwine to wet you—no more
> Oh, Lord, I want to go home—go home—

This was the old, old chant for the dead on the way to burial.

Mary Simmons loved to sing, and she never begrudged her wonderful voice to the dead. She left her room and walked the short distance to the old burying ground where she could see a group of people gathered together for the burial service. She joined the mourners, singing with all her heart the familiar comfort chant for the dead:

> No more rain gwine to wet you—no more
> No more cold gwine to cold you—no more
> Oh, Lord, I want to go home—

Soon it began to rain hard. The wind was cold, but the singing

201

never faltered. Mary took off her hat and was about to slip it under her skirt, when a tall man in a black coat stepped beside her and said, "Sister, a song like yours needs a dry cover." And he put his umbrella into her hands and stepped away.

So Mary sang on in the rain, out of her full heart, the old chant which South Carolina coastal Negroes used to sing for their dead.

When the singing was over, Mary could hear the deep voice of the preacher somewhere in the crowd of people pronouncing the benediction. She bowed her head. ". . . and the blessing of God Almighty abide with you all forever. Amen."

The Amen was like the shout of an army of voices. The ground shook. But when Mary raised her head and looked about, she saw that she was standing alone in the rain in a little graveyard that had been forsaken long ago. There had been no funeral in that grass-grown place for years and years.

She was frightened, and she hurried, stumbling, from the unkempt spot. When she got to her own door, she realized that she still had the umbrella in her hand. She looked back down the darkening road for the tall man in the black coat, but there was no one in the road. There was no one anywhere in sight. Rain and twilight together created their own gray emptiness.

Puzzled and afraid, Mary wondered what would happen next. She thought perhaps some ghost would come in a clap of thunder and snatch the umbrella out of her hands. But nothing happened. So she walked into her room and stood the umbrella in the corner. There it stood for years. Mary used it in wet weather, and it kept her dry. But it was not for lending.

"Mary Simmons, God rest her tired old bones, has been, herself, these forty years, asleep in some such Sea Island burying ground as she described to me. She was for ten years Mrs. Bennett's capable, old-fashioned cook. I stood on the wharf and watched the convoy row away, singing, bearing her body back to the place of her birth and girlhood."—*John Bennett.*

The Yellow Ribbon

JOHN loved Jane. They lived next door to each other, and they went to first grade together, and John loved Jane very much. Jane wore a yellow ribbon around her neck every day.

One day John said, "Why do you wear the yellow ribbon?"

"I can't tell," said Jane. But John kept asking, and finally Jane said maybe she'd tell him later.

The next year they were in the second grade. One day John asked again, "Why do you wear the yellow ribbon around your neck?" And Jane said maybe she'd tell him later.

Time went by, and every once in a while John asked Jane why she wore the yellow ribbon, but Jane never told. So time went by.

John and Jane went through high school together. They loved each other very much. On graduation day John asked Jane please to tell him why she always wore the yellow ribbon around her neck. But Jane said there was no point in telling on graduation day, so she didn't tell.

Time went by, and John and Jane became engaged, and finally Jane said maybe she would tell him on their wedding day.

The wedding day came, and John forgot to ask. But the next day John asked Jane why she wore the yellow ribbon. Jane said, "Well, we are happily married, and we love each other, so what difference does it make?" So John let that pass, but he still *did* want to know.

Time went by, and finally on their golden anniversary John asked again. And Jane said, "Since you have waited this long, you can wait a little longer."

Finally Jane was taken very ill, and when she was dying John asked again, between sobs, "*Please* tell me why you wear the yellow ribbon around your neck."

"All right," said Jane, "you can untie it."

So John untied the yellow ribbon, and Jane's head fell off.

This story is classified as "school folklore" because children love to tell it. It always makes a hit told to a group in a darkened room. But it is not of school origin. It is the offspring of an old European folk motif featuring the mysterious red thread around someone's neck. The mystery is solved when it is revealed that the thread marks the line at which he was once decapitated.

Washington Irving used the motif in a story of the French Revolution, "The Adventure of the German Student," in his *Tales of a Traveller.*

Never

PETER RUGG was a young man who lived on Middle Street
in Boston with his pretty young wife and pretty little daughter Jenny. He was a serious, fine young man, the neighbors
said, and had but one fault. He had a terrible temper and used to
fall into violent swearing fits when things were not going his way.
He had been known to kick his way through a door in a rage and
sometimes the curses he uttered would make his wig rise up off his
head.

One day in the fall of 1770 Peter Rugg drove from Boston to
Concord to visit a friend. He drove a beautiful black horse hitched
to a "chair," a kind of open chaise in use in those days, with one

seat wide enough for one or sometimes two. Little Jenny, who was then about ten years old, went with him.

On the way back a heavy rainstorm overtook them, and Peter Rugg took shelter for himself and his child for a while with friends, the Cutters, in Menotomy, which is now Arlington.

"Stay the night," said Mr. Cutter kindly. "It is raining harder than ever."

But Peter Rugg was beginning to feel impatient with the delay.

"Thank you," he said, "I must get home tonight."

"But this is a terrible night, Mr. Rugg," said Cutter. "It's black as pitch outside, and the storm grows worse."

"Let it get worse!" said Peter Rugg. "I must get home tonight."

"It's no night for a child in an open chair!" said Mr. Cutter.

Peter Rugg lost his temper with this persistence. "I'll get home tonight, *or I'll never get home!*" he yelled, with a string of oaths. And he walked out of the house in the downpour, hitched up the horse, lifted the little girl into the seat, and tore off through the tempest without another word.

But Peter Rugg did not get home that night, and he never got home. His young wife waited despairingly for weeks, waited and watched at the windows; but Peter Rugg never came. One night she was roused from sleep by the sound of a horse approaching at a furious pace.

"At last he has come!" she thought.

She leaped out of bed and rushed to the window. It was indeed Peter Rugg. He was driving full speed past his own house, with the little girl beside him. But he could not stop the horse. He looked with longing up at the windows and the beloved wife, but there was no time to speak. He could not stop the horse, and Mrs. Rugg watched them disappear in the dark night, as if swept along by the rain and wind which seemed instantly to follow them.

Young Mrs. Rugg died shortly after this—partly from loneliness and partly from heartbreak after seeing the look of longing and despair in her young husband's face as he was irrevocably carried away from her into the dark.

For years after this, people used to meet Peter Rugg and his little girl driving fast along some dark road. He never stopped except to ask the way to Boston.

"I have lost the way to Boston," he would say. "I must get home tonight." Whoever stopped and gave him directions, in fact whoever *saw* Peter Rugg, was always overtaken by storm within an hour. For this reason those who became familiar with his appearance called him "the storm breeder."

Sometimes Peter Rugg would pull up at some roadside inn and go inside to ask his way. "Can you tell me the way to Boston?" he would ask. "I am in great haste. I must get home tonight." But he was not popular with the innkeepers. Sometimes they were very short with him, for he never bought food or drink or stayed the night. He entered only to ask the way to Boston.

This sort of thing happened all over New England. Peter Rugg was seen driving the roads of Massachusetts and Connecticut and Rhode Island. People in Providence and in Hartford and in Newburyport got used to meeting him. Even in the New Hampshire hills late travelers were sometimes stopped by Peter Rugg and were asked his desperate question. People tried to avoid him, for inevitably storm, rain, wind, thunder, and lightning followed on his heels.

In the last 185 years Peter Rugg has wandered farther from home than ever. People see him on Route 40 in the Middle West, driving an old Model-T roadster with the little girl beside him. Tourists overtaking him turn their heads to gawk at the old Model T and continue to stare at the neat, quaintly dressed young man and child. Perhaps fifty miles farther on they will overtake another ancient Model T, and when they turn to look are dumfounded to see that it is the same young man and child.

"That's Peter Rugg," gas-station attendants tell them if they speak of the experience. But they seldom tell them anything more, for nobody likes to tell a traveler that he is going to have an accident. Whoever sees Peter Rugg twice in the phantom Model T is bound to meet up with an accident.

Five Drowned

THE worst shipping disaster in Newfoundland happened in 1914. There was a ship to the Ice that year; her name was the *Newfoundland,* and she lost seventy-seven out of 200 men of her crew. The men left the ship on the thirtieth of March, and they went out on the Ice to kill seals, but a storm came up, and it lasted all that day and all the next—two days it lasted—and they couldn't get back to the ship. So when the storm was over, the other ships came in, and the crews went through the Ice and they picked up the dead. Seventy-two there were; they got seventy-two. But five were missing and they never got them. They were drowned for sure, everybody said.

The next year the *Newfoundland* didn't go to the Ice at all. She wasn't allowed to go. She was an unlucky vessel after this disaster, and the spell had to be broken or she would drown more men. So she was rebuilt and changed and given a new name. This was called "taking off the curse."

But in 1916 she went out again with a new name. Her name was the *San Blanford,* and I was one of her crew. All spring we were separated from the other ships, alone by ourselves until the thirtieth day of March. On the thirtieth evening of March we steamed up alongside another ship, the *Terra Nova.* The captain of our ship and the captain of the *Terra Nova* were brothers. It was just dusk, a foggy thick evening, and the *Terra Nova* started to blow her whistle. That was a sign to us that she had some men on the Ice somewhere who had not got aboard. So, as is the custom, our captain started to blow his whistle, too. We could hear men hello and sing out away on the Ice, and the *Terra Nova* could hear them, too. We blew the whistle, thinking they were the *Terra Nova's* men, and the *Terra Nova* blew, thinking they were our men. The blowing kept up until ten o'clock. We finally stopped blowing, and then the *Terra Nova* stopped.

The next morning I was one of the men that went aboard the *Terra Nova,* and the first thing they asked was what time our men got aboard. I said, "Oh, we hadn't any men on the Ice that day."

"Oh," they said, "yes, you *had* got men on the Ice because we saw the men; we heard them hello and sing out on the Ice, and then we saw five men walk up to the side of the ship and go aboard."

Well, we didn't know what to think of that at the time. But later some members of our crew said and swore that they saw the five men come aboard, and they knew them and they were the missing men from the *Newfoundland.* So then we knew.

"Ay, yes," said Patty Mohr, "it's laid down in tradition that when a man is lost overboard from a ship, and that ship comes to that place again on another voyage, the man will come aboard."

This is an unpublished legend by MacEdward Leach, as told to him by Patty Mohr in Flatrock, Newfoundland, in the summer of 1950.

SCREAMS

Screams are scary tales that country people love to tell in a darkened room to frighten each other and themselves. Young people, especially high school and college groups, like to tell them at parties and gatherings. Such stories end with a scream on the part of the teller, which inevitably makes everybody jump.

Oh, Deary Me

ONE evening an old woman was sitting all alone in her house. "Deary me! I'm lonely!" said she.

Just then two feet came walking in the door. They crossed the room and stood in front of her.

The old woman was too amazed to say a word. She just stared. Then two legs came walking in the door and walked across the floor and fastened themselves onto the feet. In a minute a body came in the door and attached itself to the legs.

The old woman began to feel mighty uneasy.

Soon a couple of arms came in the door and walked across the floor on their hands and hooked themselves onto the body. The old woman felt scared.

Then a great big ugly head came in and put itself on the body. "Why did you come?" said the old woman.

"To be WITH YOU."

(SCREAM)

The narrator screams here to terrify the listeners.

Miss Jenny Jones

We've come to see Miss Jenny Jones, Miss
Jenny Jones, Miss Jenny Jones.
We've come to see Miss Jenny Jones—
And how is she today?

Miss Jenny Jones is washing—she's
washing, she's washing.
Miss Jenny Jones is washing,
You cannot see her now.

We've come to see Miss Jenny Jones, Miss
Jenny Jones, Miss Jenny Jones.
We've come to see Miss Jenny Jones—
And how is she today?

Miss Jenny Jones is ironing, she's
ironing, she's ironing.
Miss Jenny Jones is ironing,
You cannot see her now.

We've come to see Miss Jenny Jones, Miss
Jenny Jones, Miss Jenny Jones.

Screams

We've come to see Miss Jenny Jones—
　　　　And how is she today?

Miss Jenny Jones is scrubbing, she's
　　　　scrubbing, she's scrubbing.
Miss Jenny Jones is scrubbing,
　　　　You cannot see her now.

We've come to see Miss Jenny Jones, Miss
　　　　Jenny Jones, Miss Jenny Jones.
We've come to see Miss Jones—
　　　　And how is she today?

Miss Jenny Jones is sick in bed, she's
　　　　sick in bed, she's sick in bed.
Miss Jenny Jones is sick in bed,
　　　　You cannot see her now.

We've come to see Miss Jenny Jones, Miss
　　　　Jenny Jones, Miss Jenny Jones.
We've come to see Miss Jenny Jones—
　　　　And how is she today?

Miss Jenny Jones is dying, she's
　　　　dying, she's dying.
Miss Jenny Jones is dying,
　　　　You cannot see her now.

After the next approach, the children chant, as usual:

We've come to see Miss Jenny Jones, Miss
　　　　Jenny Jones, Miss Jenny Jones.

The answer is:

Miss Jenny Jones lies stiff and dead, she's
　　　　stiff and dead, she's stiff and dead.
Miss Jenny Jones is dead, dead, dead.
　　　　You cannot see her now.

Spoken: Well, when can we see her?
Answer: At the funeral.

> Miss Jenny Jones is dead, dead, dead,
> > She's dead, dead, dead.
> Miss Jenny Jones is dead, dead, dead,
> > And carried to the grave.

This is a singing game in which a group of children, representing the friends and neighbors of Miss Jenny Jones, come so persistently to call upon her; one child is Miss Jenny Jones, and one impersonates the mother to answer the questions and to hide Miss Jenny Jones from view. When Jenny Jones is finally dead, she lies down, the mother stands aside, and the children carry her, by arms and legs, a short distance to her grave. At this point the group becomes a group of mourners who weep into their handkerchiefs. In a few minutes Jenny Jones rises up and chases the mourners, who scream, "The ghost! The ghost!" and run away.

As sung and played in New England, Eloise Hubbard Westcott reports that Miss Jenny Jones is Miss Jennia Jones, and she gives another and a more dramatic ending.   The group sings:

> I dreamt I saw a ghost last night,
> > ghost last night, ghost last night.
> I dreamt I saw a ghost last night,
> > under the apple tree.
>
> The ghost rose up and said to me,
> > said to me, said to me,
> The ghost rose up and said to me . . .

Here Jenny Jones rises and SCREAMS, and the rest of the players run off screaming.

It is interesting to find Jenny called Jen-ní-a in New England, for Georgia children sing, "We've come to see Miss Jenny I. Jones."

Shall I Be So?

There was an old woman, all skin and bones
M – m – m – m – m – m – m – m – m – m
And she went to church. (*spoken*)

And when she came inside the door
She saw a corpse upon the floor.
M – m – m – m – m – m – m – m – m – m
And she looked at it. (*spoken*)

217

The corpse it was all bone and skin,
The worms crawled out, and the worms crawled in,
The worms crawled over its mouth and chin.
M – m – m – m – m – m – m – m – m – m

The woman to the parson said,
"Shall I be so when I am dead?"
The parson to the woman said,
"Yes, you'll be so when you are dead."

(SCREAM)

You'd Scream Too

THERE is another, very different, kind of scream story told on dark nights around campfires. It is about a man who lived in an isolated cabin in the woods with his little girl and little boy. The man's wife was dead. Every day the man went fishing in the lake or hunting in the woods to provide food for his children. He hated to leave the children alone, but there was no help for it.

One day while he was hunting in the woods he felt a sudden fear that all was not well at home, so he hurried back. When he arrived the little girl ran into his arms, sobbing, and the little boy could not be found. He looked everywhere but never found him. And the little girl, when questioned, only wept and wept.

Time went by and, of course, the man had to go on with his fishing and hunting. About a year later one day in the woods, he felt this same sudden fear that all was not well at home, so he hurried back. When he arrived the little girl was gone. He searched high and low, far and wide, but he could not find her. Night came and the child was still lost, and the man did not know what to do.

While he was sitting alone in the room, he suddenly thought, "Why, I haven't looked in the attic!" So he decided to look in the attic. Then he thought if there was anything up there, he'd better be very quiet, so he took off his shoes.

Barefoot, he crept up the stairs in the dark—very carefully so as not to make a sound. Softly he opened the attic door at the top of the stairs, and——

(SCREAM)

Here the storyteller gives a terrible scream—and says no more. Silence falls. Finally some timid voice in the circle of listeners will usually say, "Why did he scream?"

The answer is "You'd scream too if you stepped barefoot on broken glass."

———

Oral Americana collected by Jerome Fried.

LOCAL LEGENDS AND POPULAR TALES

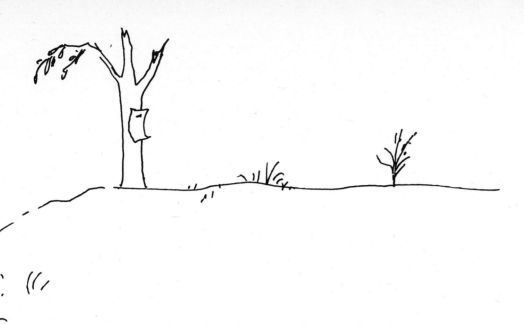

Lovers' Leaps

THE story of the lovers' leap is perhaps the favorite and most widespread of all the local legends in America. Some beautiful young Indian girl has died for love by leaping off a rock or cliff in almost every state of the Union.

There is Jump Mountain near Lexington, Virginia, where, it is said, a young Indian girl and her warrior lover jumped off together because of tribal laws against their marriage. There is a high cliff at Hot Springs, North Carolina, which local pride claims as the first Lovers' Leap to be so called in America. Here, too, the traditional young Indian couple leaped off into space because their tribes were hostile and forbade their union.

Near New Milford, Connecticut, on the Housatonic River below the falls called Metichawan, rises another precipitous cliff called Lovers' Leap, named from the story of a young Indian girl and her white lover, whom she found lost in the forest. She took him home to her father's warm fire and finally won the chief's consent to their marriage. The boy wished to make a farewell visit to his own people first, however, but promised to return to his love as soon as possible.

223

Months went by and he did not come. Winter passed and the girl began to grieve. Spring came and she began to sicken. Her father's impatience and anger at this apparent desertion grew apace, and finally he demanded that his daughter marry a neighboring chief. But on her wedding day, adorned with her bridal finery, the girl sprang into her canoe and headed down the river for the roaring rapids.

Just as the frail canoe swirled into the white waters, she heard a song above her head. She looked up. There was her true love come back at last, standing on the cliff above. He saw what was happening and leaped from the rock to join her.

This same story is told of a young Indian girl and an English sailor whom she met on the shore near Jamestown, Virginia. He too went home for a farewell visit, and the young girl watched the sea for his return for a year. One day from a high rock she saw the ship approaching. It was a day of wind and storm. She could only watch the ship break up on the rocks below, and she saw his drowning face float by. In despair she leaped into the foaming waters to join him.

There are at least eight lovers' leaps in Texas; six of them have stories about the beautiful Indian girl who jumps off a cliff rather than be separated from her own true love. There are four lovers' leaps in Nebraska. One of them, a light-colored stone cliff about 100 feet high in Knox County, Nebraska, is called the Maiden's Leap. The legend associated with this place is about a young Santee Indian girl whose father promised her in marriage to an old chief. She, however, loved a young and handsome warrior, and rather than marry anyone else, she took one of her father's horses and rode pell-mell off the cliff. The Maiden's Leap is a favorite place for Sunday picnickers, and the face of the cliff is scrawled with the names of modern lovers (nonleaping).

There is a cliff at Newport, Rhode Island, named for the leap of another hopeless young Indian pair. The Maiden's Cliff in the Catskills almost tells its own story. There are other Lovers' Leaps at Mackinac, Michigan, at Chattanooga, Tennessee, in the Berkshires of Massachusetts, in the Black Hills of South Dakota. All these stories are white men's stories *about* Indian lovers. The tales do not exist in the folklore and legend of the tribes themselves.

Occasionally, however, there is a Lovers' Leap named for some non-Indian girl. There is a high rock called Lover's Leap on Wissahickan Creek near Philadelphia from which a brokenhearted girl leaped to her death because she was abandoned by her lover. And Deborah's Rock near Reading, Pennsylvania, is named for the desperate girl who there leaped to her death for the sake of love.

Humbug

THE town of North Bloomfield, California, used to be named Humbug back in the old gold-rush days.

A man walked into town one night, went into a bar, ordered a drink, and began to brag about striking it rich. He was so tired of scraping up gold, he said, that he had to come to town for a drink!

"Why, there's gold there, lying right on the ground!" he said. "When the wind blows up a bit, gold dust blows right up your nose and down your throat! Every time you sneeze you lose money!"

A lot of gold-rushers rushed out there the next day to work the stream the braggart had described. In about two days they named the place Humbug and went back.

Spuyten Duyvil

SPUYTEN DUYVIL is a little tidewater creek that runs across the northern tip of Manhattan Island, separating Manhattan from the mainland. It is about a mile long and connects the Hudson and Harlem rivers. Spuyten Duyvil means, in Dutch, spitting devil, spitting, seething, squirting, or swirling devil. And the creek was so named for its violent little tide rip which occurred twice daily. But another story says that Spuyten Duyvil was named for the words of a brave Dutchman who was drowned in it while performing his duty.

Anthony Van Corlaer was trumpeter in the garrison at New Amsterdam back in the old days when the Dutch still held Manhattan. Old Peter Stuyvesant had appointed him official trumpeter to call the people together to hear news, warnings, or the statement of laws. It was said that no enemy would come near the place for fear of being struck deaf by Anthony's blasts.

One night old Peter got news that the English were going to attack the little Dutch colony. He sent Anthony with his trumpet to alert all the villages along the Hudson and call the people to arms. So Anthony headed north. He carried his trumpet slung across one shoulder, and a heavy stone bottle filled with Dutch courage hung from his belt.

It was a pitch-black, stormy night by the time Anthony Van Corlaer got as far as the northern tip of Manhattan, and there was no ferryman in sight to take him across the creek. He called loudly up and down, but no one answered. After some time he realized that no help was coming; no ferry would cross that water that night. But Anthony, undaunted, said he would swim that creek in spite of the devil (*en spuyt den duyvil*).

He plunged into the cold water. And the Devil, who had heard himself called, grabbed him by the leg and pulled him under.

Anthony gave a terrific blast on his trumpet, and the Devil let go. But the poor man had not enough breath to blow and swim the swirling waters too, and he was drowned.

For years after this, people in that neighborhood used to say they could hear Anthony's trumpet blowing louder than the wind on stormy nights.

This story is a wonderful and horrible example of the trumped-up local legend, the story concocted to explain the name. Who was there that night to hear Anthony Van Corlaer say he would swim the creek in spite of the Devil? Whom did the Devil tell? It is the reverse of the true folk name which *begins* with the fact. The real reason for naming a place is the folk name of the place. But the violent little spitting devil at Spuyten Duyvil is not seen today at the turn of the tide. The creek has been deepened and is used as a ship channel.

The Phantom Ship of the Hudson

THERE is a phantom ship that sails the Hudson River, and those who have seen her have different tales to tell.

Some people say it is the *Flying Dutchman,* and that old Captain Vanderdecken has found peace at last from the curse of eternal wandering. Once every year the ship is seen sailing up the river. The story is that Captain Vanderdecken found in some little Hudson River village a pink-cheeked buxom Dutch girl with blond braids who loved him dearly. Everyone knows that true love will break the spell of any curse. This is what happened, they say, for the ship never goes back.

Others say it is Henry Hudson's *Half Moon* which sails up the river once a year on some thunderous summer night. She gets as far as the Catskills and stops. The ghostly crew go ashore in a small boat to drink and make merry. Some say they have been heard singing and carousing in the hills.

Some say it is Captain Kidd coming back for the treasure which he hid in a cave in the steep cliff called Cro' Nest. Still others call it the storm ship of the Tappan Zee, because to see her is a storm warning.

The Tappan Zee is a broad part of the Hudson, about ten miles long, between what is now Croton Point and Irvington, that varies from two to three miles in width. The widest part is between Nyack and Tarrytown. They say the specter ship suddenly appears at night in a high gale out of the dark shadow of the Palisades and speeds back and forth from shore to shore in complete silence. If ever you see her, shimmering white in the moonlight on a summer night, go home.

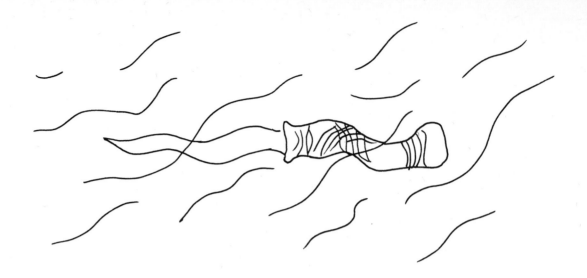

Wokun

IN THE old days the southern shores of Nova Scotia from Halifax to Cape Sable were called Kespoogit by the Micmac Indians: Kespoogit, or "land's end." Through the dark forest land of Kespoogit, near the southern tip, flows a river which the Scottish settlers named the Clyde (for their own Clyde), but which the old Micmacs called Oonigunsuk, or "good portage." It was a good waterway into the deep woodlands, to their winter camping grounds and to good hunting and fishing.

The brooks and creeks of Oonigunsuk took the Indians still deeper into the forests and into other waterways by which they traveled far inland. There was Lake Sebim, "the great wide waters," where the Micmacs camped in the winter; the Musquash, where there were muskrats; the Madashach, where there were fat porcupines; and Wabei, or "daybreak," so called because the Indians had to leave that lake at daybreak if they wished to travel down the Ministegeksebo (now the Barrington River) and reach its mouth in one day.

Into the Oonigunsuk runs a creek which the Micmacs named Wokun because lying on a rock beneath its brown water is an

Indian knife which they could never reach, not even with the tips of their fingers. (*Wokun* is the Micmac word for knife.) An old Micmac Indian I knew saw it in his youth when he went logging for the English. He reached for it eagerly, but it lay just beyond his fingertips. He reached again and again, but his fingers could never touch it.

Then he knew it was the bloody knife that had slipped from the hand of a dying Indian generations ago. He knew it had lain on that rock long before he ever saw it, and that not even the fierce spring torrents could wash it away. It had become a part of the rock; nothing could remove it. He tried to reach it again and again, but the water was deep, deep, deep. Yet he knew it was *not* very deep. So he gazed in awe at the sharp blade and remembered the story he had heard when he was a child living with his people on the shores of Lake Sebim.

Long ago two Micmac men got into a fight on the banks of this small creek. They fought fiercely and tore at each other with their knives, until one of them lost his footing and was driven into the water. His bloody knife slipped from his hand and sank down through the water to a rock beyond his reach. He clawed and thrashed in the bloody water, but the knife lay just beyond his fingertips. Finally he too sank down and lay as still as the knife on the rocks beneath.

Later his own people came and found him and lifted his body from the cold creek. But when they reached for the knife beside him, no one could touch it. It lay forever beyond reach.

The long years went by, and the Micmacs named that creek Wokun for the mysterious knife which they could see through the brown water. Today the white men call this creek Bloody Creek, but whether they named it from the Micmac story or for some skirmish of their own, I do not know.

This is an unpublished legend by Marian Doane Robertson, told to her as a child by James Michael, Micmac Indian, who was then seventy-nine years old.

The Lincoln Totem Pole

IN A LITTLE village named Tongas on Tongas Island off the coast of Alaska, one day the Raven clan of the Tlingit Indians raised up a totem pole fifty feet high, topped by the carved figure of Abraham Lincoln. This happened sometime following the year 1867. And the story is this:

In the old days the Tlingit Indians used to hold slaves and trade in slaves, and some of them served as slaves themselves. The Eagle clan of the Tlingit especially became very wealthy. They used to go on forays and expeditions even as far south as California, capturing prisoners from neighboring Indian tribes, whom they would hold or trade as slaves. And as time went on, there was great rivalry and bad feeling between the Raven clan and the wealthy, aggressive, slave-trafficking Eagles.

In 1867 a United States Revenue cutter came to the little island of Tongas bearing the story of the Emancipation Proclamation of 1863 and the Thirteenth Amendment of 1865 which enforced it. The Ravens listened to the tale and decided to make a big thing of it.

Carefully their artists carved out the big figure of Lincoln in his tall hat; and when it was finished, up went the huge Lincoln totem pole—to the honor of the Great Emancipator and to the shame of

the Eagles. The story of Abraham Lincoln and the freeing of the slaves was taken over as one of the permanent legends of the Raven clan. It was recited at the winter festivals; and the carved figure at the top of the pole helped the people remember.

In 1867, too, the Tlingit Indians came under the jurisdiction of the United States, along with Alaska, and thus all slaves among them were freed by the provisions of the famous proclamation.

There are three Lincoln totem poles still in existence. The one from Tongas was recently removed to the museum at Juneau; a copy of it was erected at Saxman in 1940; and one is preserved in the Illinois State Museum at Springfield.

Chestnuts

DID you hear about the little moron who saw the headline in the paper *Americans Fight With Axis* and then went around collecting money to buy guns and ammunition for the soldiers?

The little moron was born in America in the 1930's and grew up during World War II, but he was already centuries old at birth. Old jokes never die. People not only love their old jokes, but people everywhere love the same ones! Little Moron is just another name for the beloved world-wide fool, booby, noodle, or numskull.

There were two little morons who went fishing and caught so many fish that they wished they could find the same place the next day. "We'll find it," said one little moron. "I put a mark on the boat right over the place we were fishing."

"But how do you know we'll get this same boat tomorrow?"

This story seems to have been told all over the world wherever any two people ever went fishing together. It is as old as the early Buddhistic writings in India and China. It was current all over Europe in the Middle Ages and is now told almost everywhere in North America as being said by "an old man my grandfather knew."

One little moron was telling another his terrible dream. He dreamed that he stepped on a nail which pierced his foot. "Well, why do you sleep barefoot?" said the other.

This one is at least 1,400 years old. It is one of the jests of the Greek sage Hierocles of the fifth century A.D., whose jests were already chestnuts, from India and perhaps Egypt, when he recorded them. The chestnut about the man whose horse died just as he got it trained to live without food is also one of the jests of Hierocles. It was common throughout Europe long before it spread to America as one of hundreds of pointed little anecdotes all beginning with the words "Did you hear about the man who . . . ?"

234

The one about guarding the door, in "Jean Sot," the next story in this book, is another chestnut. It was told as one of the escapades of Giufa, the Sicilian booby, at least 300 years ago.

Jean Sot

ONE DAY Jean Sot's mother had to go out on an errand. "You dress the chicken for dinner while I'm gone," she said to her son.

Jean Sot was happy to do this for his mother. When that good woman returned to the house, there was one of the dooryard hens dressed in the baby's best dress and sitting quietly in the high chair at the table.

Another day Jean's mother sent him on an errand, and he put on his best suit and hat before starting out.

"It looks like rain, Jean," said the mother. "Don't let the rain spoil your best suit and hat."

So Jean Sot started out. On the way back, just as he was crossing the bridge over the bayou, it started to rain—a heavy downpouring rain. He remembered what his mother had said, but he saw no shelter anywhere. The rain was already soaking into his suit, so he jumped into the bayou up to his neck to keep the rain from getting on his suit. Then he realized that his hat was still being rained on, so he took it off and held it under the water. He was an obedient young boy.

"Guard the door, now," his mother said one day, as she left the house to go to town. Jean said he would. She was gone so long, however, that Jean thought he had better go look for her. But he did not forget about guarding the door. He just took it off the hinges and carried it with him.

235

As he was going along, with the door on his back, he saw seven big rough men approaching, carrying with them a heavy sack. Jean thought the sack was surely full of money and that the men must be robbers. He was very frightened, and he thought he had better hide in a tree until they passed by.

So Jean started to climb. It was a hard job to climb a tree with a house door on his back, but he finally made it. Just in time, too.

But instead of passing by, the seven robbers stopped under that very tree and sat down in a circle and began to count out and divide the money.

"This for me—this for you—this for you—" the chief of the robbers was counting, as he made a little pile of money in front of each man.

"This for me—this for you—this for you—" he counted.

"And one for *me!*" cried Jean Sot.

"Who's that?" The men listened and heard nothing but the leaves rustling.

"This for me—this for you—this for you—" the chief began counting again.

"And one for *me!*" cried Jean Sot.

"Who's that?" cried the chief. "I'll wring the fool's neck!"

This frightened Jean Sot so much that he began to tremble, and he trembled so hard that the door slipped off his back and fell down on the robbers. The seven robbers jumped to their feet and ran off. They thought it must be the Devil himself after them if he could throw doors around like that.

Then Jean Sot climbed down from the tree and picked up all the money and went home with it.

"Not so foolish, after all," said his mother.

Jean Sot is the beloved world-wide numskull in Louisiana Cajun and Louisiana Creole guise. The name means Foolish John. Sometimes it is spelled Jean Sotte. He is the foolish boy who takes all directions literally and in spite of (or because of) his incredible stupidity comes out on top in the end.

Roommates

ONE DAY a trapper got caught in a blizzard. It was cold, the wind was piercing, and the snow was coming so thick that he couldn't see his way more than a foot in front of him. He could not even find the trail for home. He kept stumbling up rough hills and slipping down into little icy hollows.

At last, exhausted, he decided to give up and look for some kind of shelter near at hand. He felt his way in the snow along the face of a huge boulder, thinking he might shelter under some jutting ledge of rock. Suddenly he felt an opening—a big opening. He stepped into it and found himself in a cave. It was dark, but he was safe from the obliterating snow and piercing wind. There were dry leaves under his feet. This was wonderful! He lay down, rolled up in the position all hunters know, and went to sleep.

Suddenly he was startled from sleep by a great sound of thrashing around and grunting in the cave. He reached out his hand in the dark and felt something big and warm and rough and furry.

It was a bear. He had stumbled into the cave of a hibernating bear. Lucky me! he thought to himself, understanding at once the wonderful warmth of the place. But what was wrong with this old fellow—thrashing around and complaining in his sleep?

Suddenly he remembered the old tale that bears suck their paws during the long winter sleep. He felt around in the dark until he found a paw and stuck it back in the animal's mouth. "Mmm," said the bear and then was quiet. And they both went to sleep.

This story used to be a common hunters' tale all over the United States wherever there were bears and blizzards. It has been told for fact from Maine to Arkansas and the Rockies. It is a common European and legendary saints' anecdote. Various North American Indian groups have the tale also.

The Talking Mule

ONCE there was a man had a mule named Sam. The mule worked hard all week, but on Sunday the man and his wife went to church and came home and ate dinner, and the mule rested.

One Sunday the man had to go to a funeral. He told his little boy to go down to the stall and put the saddle on Sam.

So the boy went down to the stall.

"Move over, Sam," he said. Then he took the bridle off the hook.

"For gosh sake, have I got to work on Sunday?" said Sam.

The boy dropped the bridle and ran out of there fast. He ran into the house and told his father the mule talked.

"For gosh sake, can't you even saddle the mule?" said the man.

"Sam don't want to work Sundays," said the boy.

The man was pretty mad at the boy for telling a story like that. So he went to saddle the mule himself. He picked up the bridle where the boy had dropped it.

"Move over, Sam," he said.

"You say 'Move over, Sam' but you don't bring me anything to eat," said the mule.

The man dropped the bridle and ran out of there fast. The little dog, who had followed him, ran too.

"I never heard a mule talk before," said the man.

"Me neither," said the little dog.

Then that man did run. He ran into the house and slammed the door.

"The mule talked," said the man.

"What!" said his wife.

"I said I never heard a mule talk before and the dog said 'me neither,' " said the man.

"Ridiculous!" said the wife.

"What's ridiculous about that?" said the cat. "Who ever heard a mule talk?"

This story is told in one form or another wherever there are Negroes. The Ashanti of Africa begin their series of talking objects with a log, or with a bundle of sticks being carried home for firewood. In Ethiopia it is a goat. All over the southern United States it is a mule. This story is based on a Negro folk tale from St. Helena Island, South Carolina, collected by Elsie Clews Parsons and published in the *Journal of American Folklore*, Vol. 38, (1925), pp. 225–226.

Why Lizard Can't Sit

ONE DAY Lizard and Frog were trying to squeeze through a crack in a split-rail fence. This happened long, long ago when Lizard and Frog sat down the same way. Lizard used to sit on his bottom, propped up in front, the way dogs and frogs sit today.

"I'll get through this here crack, God willing!" said Frog. He tried and he struggled, and he finally squeezed through.

"I'll squeeze through this here crack, God willing or not!" cried Lizard. He tried and he struggled, but a rail fell down and mashed him flat. Lizard never sat up again after that.

Never Mind Them Watermelons

ONCE there was a man who said he didn't believe in ghosts, didn't believe in haunts, didn't believe in haunted houses. Another man said he'd give him a whole wagonload of watermelons if he would spend the night in a certain old empty house down the road.

The man said, sure, he'd sleep there, so he picked up his matches and tobacco and set out. He went in the house and lighted his pipe. He sat down in a chair and started to read the paper.

Pretty soon something sat down beside him and said, "Ain't nobody here but you and me?"

"Ain't gonna be nobody but you in a minute," said the man. So he jumped out the window and started to run. He ran pretty fast, overtook two rabbits going the same way. Pretty soon something caught up with him and said, "Well, you makin' pretty good speed."

"Oh, I can run faster than this," said the man—and did.

When he passed the man who gave him the dare, he said, "Never mind about them watermelons."

The Goat That Flagged the Train

ONCE there was a man who had a goat. It was a smart goat —but a nuisance. Every time the man's wife hung the wash out to dry, the goat would eat a towel or a shirt or something off the line.

The man decided he would have to get rid of the creature, but the children loved it so much he kept putting it off. Then one day he came to it. The goat ate his favorite red shirt right off the line! That man was so mad he took the goat down and tied him to the railroad track, just before train time—and left him there.

But that goat saved his own life. He coughed up the shirt and flagged the train!

In some versions of this story it is a red flannel shirt; in some it is a silk shirt; in some it is three red shirts, material unspecified.

The first time I ever heard about this goat I was a small child in New York. I heard a song, "The Goat," of the barbershop-quartet variety, played on an old Edison cylinder record. The story of the song enchanted me, and soon I and my friends were singing it, endlessly. The tune is the same as "And When I Die."

I was still full of the goat and his satisfying victory over man when I went to visit some cousins in Plainfield, New Jersey. They already knew the song, and what was more—they knew the goat! It was Mr. Keeley's goat, they said. (Mr. Keeley used to hire out to beat rugs.) It was Mr. Keeley's goat, and tomorrow we could go and look at it. "But Papa says he didn't really do it," they explained.

Wherever the song was heard no doubt somebody produced "the actual goat." Zora Neale Hurston reports the story in dialect as a Negro folk tale from the South in her *Mules and Men*. The riddle of the song and story about the goat that flagged the train is like the riddle about the chicken and the egg. Which came first?

Grandma'am Hinkel and the Phantom Dog

GRANDMA'AM HINKEL'S favorite story was that of the phantom dog, and she told it more often than any other. Those of her grandchildren's generation back in the early 1920's were at the time more interested in dragons, for some reason or other. She herself had more than once seen a dragon flying across the sky, snorting smoke and flame, and she insisted that the dragon's abode was in a cave that ran from the lime kiln on her farm (in Berks County, Pennsylvania) to that on the adjoining farm to the west. She could not recall just when she had last seen it, but of its existence she assured us all there was not the slightest doubt.

"Ma'am," as she was usually referred to by her children, grand-children, great-grandchildren, friends, and acquaintances, spoke very little English, though her people had been in Pennsylvania for two centuries. When I first met her in 1922 she was past eighty, but she was still alert, and her mind was well stocked with the lore of the Pennsylvania Dutch. She did not talk much but, when she did, it was in her native tongue. But whenever she spoke everyone listened, for Ma'am was loved and respected by all. (She represented the end of her generation, and there was none who did not regret the fact that with her passing there would be no one left to represent the living yesterday.) Her story of the dragon never varied, but as often as one questioned her about it, she quickly shifted to her tale of the phantom dog.

Ma'am had not seen the dog since she gave up driving the buggy herself, but while she still drove, a big dog, like a St. Bernard, rarely failed to appear as she reached the steep part of the hill down the road below the pigsty. The road is an old one, worn deep through the years, and the dog would suddenly materialize out of nothing and trot along the top of the right-hand bank whimpering like a baby—like the baby Ma'am had lost.

At the foot of the hill is a stream which the dog would leap across, whimpering all the way. A hundred yards beyond the creek was the line fence of the next farm. This the dog would also leap across, and disappear into nothingness. The minute he started to cross the line he began to vanish, the portions beyond the fence becoming invisible as he crossed it. Ma'am would drive on, wondering, but happy at the companionship, and content.

On the way home, when Ma'am reached the line fence, the great dog would again appear and run along the top of the high bank by her side, all the time whimpering like her baby. And then, just as they reached the point where the hill began to ease, the phantom animal would disappear.

Ma'am could not remember just when she had last driven the buggy, but she did know that she had never seen the dog when in an automobile—only when in a buggy.

This is an unpublished story by William J. Phillips as he heard it from Grandma'am Hinkel herself on the farm in Berks County, Pennsylvania, in 1922. The name Hinkel is fictitious.

The Dough Image

I REMEMBER a scene at a farmhouse at which I was staying in Berks County, Pennsylvania, one January night in 1924. Near one end of "The Room," as it was called, was a large stove. Behind the stove, on a horse blanket spread out on the floor, lay Isaac Yoder, the farmer. Seated facing the stove, with our feet on the ornate nickeled heat ring, were his nephew and I. I do not remember how the conversation got around to witchcraft, but I do remember asking Ike if he had ever known of any witches.

246

"Sure," he said to me. "That's how we killed old Jake Wetzel."

Ike's father, Old Ike, had been prominent in the neighborhood —a director of the Reading Fair, a member of the school board, road boss, a deacon in the church, and otherwise an important citizen. He had bought a rundown 163-acre farm on a heavy mortgage, and in ten years he, his wife, and their eleven children had paid off the mortgage, put the buildings in prime condition, and had so improved the farm that it was a power in the countryside.

For no apparent reason a wasting illness came upon Old Ike. His appetite kept up, but he became thinner and thinner and weaker and weaker. Local doctors could do nothing; specialists were called in from near-by large cities, and they could do nothing. Finally Old Ike was told that he could not live, and that he had better make his will and put his affairs in order. He told the doctors that he did not want to die, and asked if they would have any objections if he called in a witch (*hex* is the Pennsylvania Dutch word for witch). The physicians said they did not mind, but asked permission to stay in the room while the hex-doctor was there to observe his treatment. And so the hex was summoned.

"Have you any enemies?" was the first question.

"None that I know of," said the sick man.

Then, going into a kind of trance, the hex-doctor said, "I see an old man dressed in blue overalls with thin white stripes. He has a little beard on his chin, his hand shakes with the palsy, and he carries a horse blanket under his left arm."

"Oh, that's Jake Wetzel," said Old Ike.

"Has he anything against you—any reason to put a jinx on you?"

"Well," replied Old Ike, "he wanted to buy my lower cornfield, and I wouldn't sell it. I don't want to sell any part of my farm, and I *won't* sell that piece of bottomland with the stream running through it. Now that I think of it—yah, yah—right after I refused, old Jake would come into that cornfield at sundown every night; for seven nights he came and waved a horse blanket over the field three times."

"That's it," said the hex. "He has put a curse on you; you are *ferhexed* (bewitched). Now do this: have the women make an image of a man out of dough and name it the name of this man that's *ferhexed* you. Then stick it full of pins; then throw it into the fire and burn it."

All this was done, and seven days later Jake Wetzel dropped dead, and on that same day Old Ike Yoder got up out of bed and was a well man.

Note: The image might just as well have been made of wax as of dough. It was made in the image of a man so that it might represent the man who was causing the illness. It was named after the man to "fix it on him." It was stuck full of pins to torture him. And it was burned in the fire to destroy him.—*W.J.P.*

Wherever in the Dutch country any vestige of belief in witchcraft remains (and there are pockets of it) no one will say the word *hex*. This is part of the world-wide belief that if you speak of the Devil (or a witch) he will appear.

———

This is a Pennsylvania Dutch hex story from an unpublished collection by William J. Phillips, as told to him by Isaac Yoder in Berks County, Pennsylvania, in 1924. The names of characters are fictitious.

Twist-mouth Family

ONCE there was a family of people who lived in the back country far off from any town. The whole family had very funny mouths.

The father's lower lip and lower jaw stuck way, way out.

The mother's upper lip was incredibly long and hung down over the lower.

The oldest girl's mouth was twisted to the right, so that she had to talk, eat, and sing out of the right side of her mouth.

The brother's mouth was twisted to the left, so that he had to eat, talk, and laugh out of the left side of his mouth.

The youngest boy had a mouth just like anyone, but in this family that too was different.

When the children grew up, and it came time for them to go to college, the two oldest said No, they'd rather stay home with their own kin than have to go out in the world with all those straight-faced people.

But the youngest boy said Yes, he'd like to go to college. So he went.

Time went by and then the youngest boy came home for Christmas vacation.

Everybody looked forward to seeing him and hearing the news of the world. And the mother baked a big cake to celebrate.

That night the family sat around the table eating cake and listening to the adventures of the youngest brother who had been so far from home.

The cake was very good.

The father had to hold his piece way up and push it down into his mouth.

The mother had to shove her piece up under her upper lip to get it into her mouth.

The oldest girl ate daintily, poking one small piece after another into the right side of her mouth.

The brother jammed big hunks into the left side of his.

The youngest brother ate just like anyone.

It grew late and the time came to go to bed.

"Father, will you blow out the light?" said the mother.

"Yes, I will."

"Well, do," said the mother.

"Well, I will," said the father.

So the man leaned over the lamp and blew. But his under lip was so big that he could only blow up—this way—and he could not blow out the light.

"Mother, you do it," said the man.

"All right, I will."

"Well, do."

"Well, I will."

So the woman blew and blew. She blew this way— and could not blow out the lamp.

"Daughter, you do it," said the mother.

"All right, I will."

"Well, do."

"Well, I will."

So the daughter tried to blow the light out. She blew this way—and could not blow out the light.

"Here—you do it," said the girl to the brother.
"All right," said the boy, "I'll do it."
"Well, do."
"Well, I will."
So the brother tried. He blew this way—
and could not blow out the light.
"You do it," said the brother to the youngest boy.
"Sure!" said the youngest boy.
"Wh——ff" he went (like that), and the light was out.
Everybody was delighted. Now they could all go to bed.
"Wonderful thing—a college education," said the father.

I first heard this story as a small child in New York. It was told to me by the housekeeper in our family, a woman from Port La Tour, Nova Scotia. My cousins and I used to act it, and we especially enjoyed the scene with the cake. We never had a kerosene lamp to practice with; but I remember one hilarious bedtime during a Nova Scotia summer sojourn, when parents and uncles and aunts performed this scene for us with one of the kerosene lamps which were then (and still are in some small places) a part of the daily life in that province.

I heard the story again when I went to college in Indiana. A group of students "did it" as a small humorous skit in a series of impromptu student plays. I recognized it as a matter of course. It never entered my head in those days to say, "Where did you hear that story?" "Where did your old Aunt Rhody hear it?" My own child heard it again in boarding school in Pennsylvania.

Young Charlotte

Young Charlotte lived on a mountain side,
In a wild and lonely spot,
There was no house for three miles round,
Except her father's cot.

CHARLOTTE was a beautiful girl, the darling of her parents, a favorite with her friends; and she never lacked friends, fun, or pretty clothes.

One New Year's Eve there was a big party at the village inn, fifteen miles away. Charlotte was all ready and eager when young Charlie's sleigh stopped at the door to take her to the merry ball, as they called it. She had a soft silk coat on over her thin party dress, and she looked very lovely in her pretty bonnet and gloves.

Her mother ran to the door as they were leaving. "This blanket round you fold! It is a dreadful night outside, And you will die of cold."

But Charlotte would not have the blanket. "No!" she cried. She would not be seen muffled in a blanket! So off they went in the sleigh, swiftly down the mountain and over the hills, to the clear sound of the sleigh bells and the squeak of the sled runners on the frozen snow.

They drove five miles in silence; then Charlie said, shivering through his muffler, "I never saw such a night—such cold. The reins I can scarcely hold!"

And Charlotte answered only, "I am exceeding cold." Charlie cracked the whip and the horse sped on; another five miles they drove in silence. Then Charlie exclaimed that ice was freezing on his brow. Charlotte answered in a slow, faint voice, "I'm growing warmer now."

On they flew through the bright, frozen, starlit world, until at last they could see the warm window lights of the village inn and could hear the music and the voices. They pulled up before the door. Charlie jumped from the sleigh and held out his hands to Charlotte. But Charlotte did not move.

"Charlotte!" he cried. "Charlotte!" But Charlotte did not answer and she did not move. He touched her hand, and it was frozen hard as stone.

> He tore the mantle from her face,
> And the cold stars on her shone.

Quickly Charlie lifted the frozen girl out of the sleigh and carried her into the warm hall. But Charlotte had frozen to death and never spoke again.

This is folklore in reverse. Here is a ballad of known single authorship, which became so popular with people everywhere that it is now classified as a folk song. In fact, there are now more than thirty known texts; and grandmothers all over the United States

"remember" the night it happened. Some of them, even as far afield as Indiana, will give the full name of the girl and boy.

"Young Charlotte" is one of the most widely known of any purely American folk songs. There are texts from Vermont, New York, New Jersey, Pennsylvania, Ohio, Illinois, Indiana, Michigan, Wisconsin, Virginia, North Carolina, Missouri, Kentucky, Arkansas, Texas, and California. In some versions the folk have added a moralistic warning to young girls to

> . . . dress aright
> And never venture thinly clad
> On such a wintry night.

The ballad of the "Frozen Girl" is even sung in Georgia and Mississippi, where no one ever even went for a sleigh ride, let alone froze to death! It turns up variously as "Fair Charlotte," "Young Charlotte," "Frozen Charlotte," "The Frozen Girl," "The Frozen Maid."

The ballad became so popular that it was followed by a crop of dolls called Frozen Charlottes. And several Frozen Charlottes, in the party dress, can be seen in the little museum of the Germantown (Pennsylvania) Historical Society.

Old Blackie and the Little Girl

ONCE there was a little girl whose mother used to give her a bowl of bread and milk every afternoon. And the child always carried it outdoors somewhere to eat it. This seemed natural enough. Nobody thought anything of it.

Then one day the mother wondered where the little girl went every day. So she followed her and watched.

She saw the child slip off into the bushes and sit down on a log in the sun. She tinkled on the side of the bowl with her spoon, and at the sound a big blacksnake came slithering out from behind the log. It coiled up in the little girl's lap and began to eat out of one side of the bowl.

"Hello, old Blackie," said the little girl.

And the two ate the bread and milk together, each from its own side of the bowl. When the snake lapped too far over into the little girl's side of the bowl, she would tap him on the nose with the spoon and say, laughing, "You keep on your own side, Blackie!"

This was an intimate friendship. But the mother was horrified—terrified. She ran back to the house and grabbed the shotgun and came tearing back to shoot the snake. The snake tried to dash away. But she got it. She shot it dead.

The little girl just stared at her mother. She never laughed again, and she would not eat her food. She just pined away, and in about a week she died.

Here is a case of the story of the story being more interesting than the story!—for this tale is so deep-rooted in folk memory that it is always told as a true experience. It has always happened to someone's grandchild, niece, or nephew: a little girl or a little boy. The snake is a blacksnake, rattlesnake, milk snake, etc., according to locale. It is a family story or it survives vividly in the memory of some village or other rural community.

Sometimes the people explain that the snake had charmed the child into sharing its food and caused the child's death in revenge for its own. More often there is a note of awe in the telling for the gentleness of the snake with the child and the strangeness of this mystic relationship.

It is interesting that this story is one of Grimms' fairy tales (#105) in which a toad eats with the child and in return brings her gems and jewels. But it is even more ancient than this. Its origin is traced to ancient India: to a group of tales in which a serpent, grateful for food or kindness, rewards the donor with treasure.

Versions of this story have been printed from Maine and Massachusetts, from New York, Pennsylvania, Virginia, West Virginia, North Carolina, Alabama, Missouri, Arkansas. There is even an Ojibwa Indian telling reported from the Georgian Bay (Lake Huron) reservation in Ontario, which follows the type tale in such exact detail that there is little doubt of its being a take-over from white settlers.

There must be many, many other versions of this tale from other states—wherever northern Europeans have settled and put down their roots. *The author would like to know.*

Yankees

NEW ENGLAND YANKEES are smart, all right. Did you hear about the Yankee who was lying on the point of death? He just whittled it off with his jackknife and is now recovering. Even the old cows in New England give new milk. And when someone asked a New England Yankee why all New England Yankees always answer a question with another question, he said, "Do we?"

There are all kinds of Yankees, of course—all smart. There is the smart Yankee peddler; the Vermont Yankee, known for his own special brand of dry, wry humor and taciturnity; the shrewd, industrious, thrifty Yankee, often turning up in the tales as the rogue storekeeper; the wise, horse-sense Yankee philosopher, full of cracks and maxims; and the comic "green" Yankee, butt of many jokes, who sometimes goes to the big city and outwits the wise guy in the end.

One day a Yankee cheese peddler stopped at a Yankee crossroads store and found a group of village people shooting at targets outside. He thought he would make a quick penny, and proposed to the crowd that he set up his cheeses as targets at short range—he to place them and say where the shooter should stand to make the shot. All was agreed. Whoever hit the cheese should have it as a prize; whoever missed would pay the cheeseman a certain sum.

Then the man took a big round cheese and set it up behind a huge oak tree; he then paced off twelve rods of distance and told the marksman to shoot.

It takes a Yankee to outwit a Yankee, they say, and fulfill a bargain too. So what the marksman did was find a large flat stone and set it up on edge not far from the oak. Then he loaded his rifle, stood upon the spot the cheese peddler had designated, and fired. He fired at the flat stone; the bullet glanced off it and into the cheese. So the man took his prize and went home.

The Big Warm Dog

THERE was no church that certain Sunday in June, 1763. The itinerant minister did not reach the isolated little New Hampshire settlement in the mountains that day. So John and his wife decided to make the two-mile walk through the woods and up the mountain to visit John's brother. The child Sarah wanted to go with them; but it would be rough, slow going for four-year-old legs, and the parents said No, she must stay at home with the big brothers and sisters.

John and his wife started off happily together up the steep trail. Neither one noticed that Sarah had not listened to No, but was following along behind them up the path.

Sarah stopped to pick a flower here and there; she wandered aside to peer into a rabbit hole; she picked up a mica-flecked stone and watched it glint in the sun. The parents were soon out of sight. Entranced in the woodsy world, Sarah forgot all about wanting to go with them. She was used to the woods and not afraid. When she was tired she slept in the lee of a big sun-warmed boulder. At home the brothers and sisters did not worry; they thought Sarah must have been allowed to go on with the father and mother.

Late that afternoon the parents returned. "Did you leave Sarah at Uncle's?" asked the oldest girl.

"Sarah?" said the mother.

"She went with you."

The family were terrified when they realized that the little girl was alone in the woods, strayed from the path, and night falling. Neighbors, what few there were, helped in the search, but Sarah was not found.

Monday night came and still Sarah was not found. On Tuesday one man found the footprints of a child and a big bear—"*side by side*," he said with amazement. Fear for Sarah grew apace. People for miles around took up the search through the mountain forests for the little girl. On Thursday morning a man from twenty miles to the south came to the parents' house. "Call in all the searchers," he said, "and I will find the child." He had dreamed, he said, of a child sleeping under pine boughs by a brook, guarded by a bear.

Some people laughed, but the parents did not laugh. Four days had gone by and they were desperate. They were ready to snatch at any straw of hope.

So the stranger set out alone. One hour went by; two hours went by. Then a gunshot was heard—then two more shots. Three shots was the signal that the child had been found.

The stranger had followed the path of his dream and had at last found Sarah lying under a pine tree. She was weak for lack of food but not thirsty, for she had drunk from the brook. "A big warm dog," she said, had come every night to sleep beside her and keep her warm and comforted.

That little girl grew up and often told her own grandchildren about this adventure: how she put her arms around the big bear's neck and slept in his warmth, and how he saved her life in the forest. Sarah's descendants tell the story to their grandchildren today.

That Fellow

THERE was this man, a fisherman in Newfoundland, and he wanted to hire someone to go fishing with him. But help was scarce, and he couldn't find anyone. Then one day he saw a stranger walking down the street, a handsome man with good clothes. He said to him, "Is it work ye are lookin' for?" And the man said it was.

He took him on, and they went out in the vessel to fish. They agreed they would share alike with the catch and set a third share for expenses. So they fished. The strange man caught a fish now and then, and the skipper caught most that were caught. At last he said to the fellow, "Have I got to catch all your fish? Why can't you catch any?"

"Is it fish ye want?" the stranger answered him. He took the fish gaff in his hand, and he hit the port side of the boat with it. "You fish, come aboard," he shouted. All sorts and kinds of fish came flying over the gunwale. Then he hit the starboard side. "You fish, come aboard!" Fish leaped in over the starboard side, and the boat was soon full.

"Stop, you'll swamp us!" the skipper cried. The fellow held up the gaff and the fish stopped.

Then the skipper said, "What I would give for a good drink of rum to celebrate this fine run of fish!"

"And is it rum ye want?" said the man, and he took a little gimlet and bored a hole in the mast, and he held a mug under the hole, and rum ran out and filled the mug. The skipper drank it and said it was the best he ever tasted.

"Have a drink yourself," he said.

But the fellow said, "I only drink whisky." So he bored another little hole in the mast and out came whisky, and he drank it.

Soon they started for shore with the boatload of fish. The stranger tried to get a-hold of the tiller to steer the boat himself, but the skipper wouldn't let him. And so they came to land.

When it was time for dividing the fish, the fellow said, "Lay out one part for you, and one for expenses, and one for the Devil." So the skipper did that.

"One for me, one for expenses—and one for the Devil," he said. "One for me, one for expenses—and one for the Devil" until he had the whole catch divided. He put the Devil's portion on a stage (a wooden rack for drying fish used in Newfoundland). But That Fellow knocked over the stage and leaped into the sea and all the fish along with him. It was the Devil himself, no doubt.

———

This is an unpublished legend by MacEdward Leach, as told to him by Maurice Hallihan in Flatrock, Newfoundland, in the summer of 1950.

Caldera Dick

"ON THE sixth of May (1846), we again made the coast of Chile, about Caldera, the mention of which, to old whalemen, would suggest the story of Caldera Dick. It was long before my time that he flourished and fell. His career covered the whole history of the whale fisheries in the South Seas from early Colonial times, and succeeding generations of whalers tried in vain to capture him."—*Captain Benjamin Doane.*

Caldera Dick was a monstrous old bull sperm whale. There were others, big and tough and mean, but Caldera Dick was bigger, tougher, meaner—and smarter—than any other whale that ever lived. The ocean for a circuit of several hundred miles about

Caldera was his dooryard, though he didn't always stay at home. (Caldera is a little seaport on the coast of Chile.) At times he'd get around Cape Horn into the Atlantic, or he'd turn up in the Japan Sea, or you might hear of ships running afoul of him almost anywhere that boats were lowered for whales. But mostly he ranged off Caldera.

The difficulty was not in striking him and getting fast. He seemed to invite that. He'd lie still and calm as you please while a boat was put on to him, but once the dart was made and the harpoon fairly settled in his tough old hide, there was the devil to pay and no pitch hot. He seemed to have a fancy for collecting harpoons. Leastwise, he took all that came his way and never gave any back, until last of all, when he was finally bested, he was so studded with iron, it was a wonder he could float. And nobody ever thrust a lance into him, either, but the one that finished him. He was too smart for that.

His favorite game was to wait until the boat was fast, then try to get her with a flip of his flukes. Often as not, that was all there was to it: kindling wood and men flying through the air, to plop back into the sea, smashed and stunned, where old Dick could leisurely give his undivided attention to each bit of wreckage and to each desperately clinging or swimming whaleman that had survived the first blow. He'd come back among the wreckage and maneuver around through it, using his great flukes to toss any bit of it he could see or feel sky high again, as long as there was anything left that he could find.

Sometimes the boatheader would be skillful enough to sheer the boat off and escape that first thrust of the flukes. When that happened old Dick would sound, diving down into the depths, taking fathom after fathom of line after him, just as any ordinary whale might do. Then instead of coming to the surface, way off as far as the line was out, and running away, hell bent, with the boat towing after and the men hauling up to get close enough for the boatheader to use his lance and make the kill, Caldera Dick would come up right underneath the boat, so fast that the whole length of

him would shoot out of water, and the boat, along with such of the men that hadn't made it over the side in time, being chomped to death and matchwood in his jaws. Then he'd mill around through the wreckage, making little pieces out of big ones and dead men out of live ones until there was nothing left—and it was a lucky man who managed to swim fast and far enough to be out of the way, and perhaps get picked up later by the ship if it could find him.

Caldera Dick was resourceful, too. He would vary his tactics to meet the emergency, and if one method didn't work he'd try something else. He was a scourge and a terror, but he was also a terrific challenge. There were no craven hearts among the men who followed the sperm-whaling, and though boat after boat was smashed and many lives were lost in encounters with Caldera Dick, the boats never hung in the davits because of his presence but were lowered with all haste to take him on, and the men eager to have at him.

But Caldera Dick met his nemesis at last at the hands of an old Nantucket captain who devised a scheme that defied all whale philosophy. This old fellow had been bested by the great whale more than once, and it preyed upon his mind. He couldn't sleep at night, but lay in his bunk, brooding and figuring. One night a plan came to him and immediately he set to work to carry it out. The plan that came to mind was a method of taking whales that has been used by the Eskimos longer than anyone can remember, and a very simple plan it was.

First he got the cooper to make a cask—oval, instead of normal cask shape—strongly bound with iron hoops, and with the heads braced from the inside so it couldn't be stove in. The cask was then harnessed securely with ropes and a whale line made fast to it. Then the whole apparatus was stowed in the starboard boat, which was not to be lowered until they should fall in with Caldera Dick again—which happened off Caldera.

On that day the starboard boat lowered, and the captain himself took the steering oar. Caldera Dick lay quiet, as was his wont, while the boat was put on. The harpooner was told to stand up. He faced around toward the whale, readied his two harpoons, braced himself against the crotch of the boat, and as it fairly touched the whale, darted first one and then the other into him, sinking them

both home. And in almost the same instant he heaved overboard the tub of line and the cask fastened to it. The men at the oars, the pick of the ship's crew, were meanwhile following the captain's orders without even so much as a turn of the head to see what was going on, and by great skill that deadly first thrust of the flukes was avoided.

Poor Caldera Dick. Following his usual routine, sounding and coming up from below, he found no boat there to grind in his jaws —only a cask floating lightly on the water. The boat was heading back for the ship as fast as ever stout oars with strong backs to bend them could take her. So Caldera Dick gave his attention to the cask. He took it in his jaws, but it squirted out; he knocked it galley-west with his flukes, but it plopped back into the sea, unharmed. Confounded and puzzled, after several tries, Caldera Dick did what he had never done before. He tried to escape. Away he went, with the line paid out behind him, and the cask smacking along into the waves at the end of it. Dick sounded, and the cask followed him down, a powerful drag upon him. He surfaced; he sounded; he ran straight away and in circles, but always the cask was there, dragging, dragging, wearing him down. And always the whaleship managed to keep him in sight, until, utterly exhausted and gallied, he lay still upon the surface. Then the starboard boat was lowered again, and Caldera Dick succumbed to the lance of his tormentor.

This is the story of Caldera Dick as told to me when I was a small boy by my grandfather, Captain Benjamin Doane, who in the years 1845–6–7, a young man in his early twenties, was boat-steerer (harpooner) in the whaleship *Athol,* Captain James D. Coffin, out of Saint John, New Brunswick. The opening paragraph of this story is from his unpublished memoirs.

It was my grandfather's later belief that the stories of Caldera Dick, as told in the forecastles of whaling ships, were the basis of Herman Melville's great novel, *Moby Dick,* published in 1851.— *Benjamin D. Doane.*

The Piper

THIS is a true story from Cape Breton, Nova Scotia, told by Mrs. Dave Patterson. "It happened to my grandfather," she said.

My grandfather's father was a poor man, and when his wife died, leaving him with one son, he married a widow woman who was well off, and she had two sons. She was mean to his son. She made him eat in the kitchen, and she made him sit there and would not let him come into the room with the rest. Her own sons played the pipes fine. She bought them two sets of pipes, and she paid a lot for them, and all the stepson had was a miserable old chanter. He couldn't play very well.

One day he was out on the hills tending the cows and trying to play on the chanter, when who should he see but one of those little fairy men. And this one said to him, "Do you want to play as well as your brothers?" And the boy said he did.

"Well," said the little man, "put your fingers in my mouth." So he put his fingers in the little man's mouth. When he picked up the chanter to play again, he made such marvelous music that he charmed the fishes out of the water, and the little birds from the nest. But when he went home he said nothing about this. He sat in the kitchen as usual.

One day soon after this a man came there to hire one of the brothers to play the pipes on his steamer to entertain the people. He had heard that these boys were good pipers.

"Play up," he said to them, "so I can choose."

So they played, in turn, and when they had finished he said to the mother, "Who is that fellow I see out in the kitchen?"

"Oh, he's the boy that tends the cows," she said.

"Well, I see he has a chanter," said the man, "let's hear *him* play."

"Oh, he can't play," said the woman. "All he makes is noise on his miserable chanter."

"Let's hear him anyway," the man said. So the boy was called in and given one of the big pipes, and he played so wonderfully that even the stepmother had to admit that he was better than her own sons. He got the job, of course, and became the piper on the steamer.

One day when the steamer was eighteen miles off shore, it began to leak. The captain did not know what to do. Then the boy said to him, "I'll play distress music so loud that they will hear it on shore." He went up on the upper deck, and he played distress music so loud that they heard him on shore. And they sent out a boat from the land and rescued the passengers. After that the boy came ashore and settled in this valley, and all his sons were great pipers because they learned from him. And that was my grandfather.

This is a legend by MacEdward Leach as told to him by Mrs. Dave Patterson at Benacadie Pond, Cape Breton Island, Nova Scotia, in the summer of 1950. It appears in *Studies in Folklore in Honor of Distinguished Professor Stith Thompson,* edited by W. Edson Richmond, Bloomington, Indiana University Press, 1957.

Black Bartelmy

ONE of the grimmest pirate tales in all North America is centered around Cape Forchu on the southwest coast of Nova Scotia. Cape Forchu is a bleak, treeless, jagged spit of black rocks, originally named Fourchu by the French explorer Champlain for its forked shape. Today there is a lighthouse on it, but 300 years ago it was populated only by gull and gannet. Three miles south of Cape Forchu, where the Atlantic and the Bay of Fundy so treacherously merge, lies a dangerous ledge of rocks, called the Roaring Bull from the sound of its churning waters.

To Cape Forchu for some untold reason came Black Bartelmy from Tripoli, a pirate of evil repute. "He slit his wife from ear to ear, and drowned his children with a cheer," and then took to sea with a crew as murderous and evil as himself.

Bartelmy's career as a pirate was highly successful, for the story is that the ship, as she approached Cape Forchu, was loaded with treasure. Five hundred chests were filled with jewels and gold. A thick Fundy fog lay over the water, and the treacherous Fundy tide took hold of the ship, and almost as soon as Bartelmy heard the Roaring Bull, they had crashed upon it.

"There's land to starboard, Ben," cried Bartelmy. "We'll load the boat and go."

Ben was Bartelmy's mate: Ben the Hook (his arm was missing from the crook). The pair set to with glee and murdered the crew. Ben's hook did a quick, gory job.

Once inside the cape there would be calm water, and the two bowed their backs to the oars to land their precious hoard of gold and jewels. It was a long, slow, and heavy pull, but they made it. They landed on the inner side of Cape Forchu and pulled the boat ashore. Without rest they searched for a place to hide the treasure, and at last beneath a huge and jutting rock they found a cave. One by one they hauled the heavy chests to safe hiding, and then piled boulders across the mouth of the cave.

It only took a minute for Bartelmy to murder Ben. Then Bartelmy sat down on a rock and laughed, and the gulls screeched over his head. He soon realized that he could not stay there, foodless and exposed. So he walked forth along the edge of the water, trying to spy some little town up the sheltered harbor to which he might row.

But Bartelmy did not know his Cape Forchu. Suddenly he was caught in a sucking quicksand and could not get out. There was no one to hear his last despairing curse. Only the gulls screeched over his head—until the head too disappeared.

Black Bartelmy still haunts the Cape and the Roaring Bull, and

still reaches out to murder good men. Sometimes in bitter winter storm, just at sunset, the keeper of the light will see a flare go up in the direction of the Roaring Bull. This usually happens just as he is feeling his way, hand over hand, along the guideline from his warm house to the tall lighthouse which stands with its feet in foaming surf. The tide has always just turned, and the Roaring Bull is just visible, its breakers foaming white on the black water.

A second flare rises; the revolving light pinpoints for one moment a vessel breaking up on the Roaring Bull. The keeper calls the lifeboat crew; the five men launch their boat in the icy breakers and take to the oars. They head straight for the ledge, three miles off shore, watching the warm lights of home recede as the scudding spray freezes on their hats and shoulders. But as they approach the vessel in distress, they are more terrified than sea or storm or raging waters ever made them. For what they see is a high-pooped ancient galleon stripped of sail, and one evil, grinning man looking down at them.

At this point high thunderous breakers toss the small boat broadside to the seas; it fills and flounders and every man is drowned.

This used to happen periodically off Cape Forchu, they do say, and no one knows when it will happen again.

OTHER

AMERICAN FOLK

TALES

Kunikdjuaq

A BEAR STORY OF THE INUIT

WAY NORTH in Alaska there was a little village of the Eskimo people who call themselves Inuit. (*Inuit* means men.) There were only a few little houses in the village strung along the cold waters of the Arctic shore, and in one of them lived a lonely old woman. She had no strong young son of her own to go hunting and fishing for her or bring home meat and fish.

One day she found a little white polar bear cub all alone on the ice. Someone must have killed his mother, she thought, so she took him home.

The cub's name was Kunikdjuaq. The old woman fed him as best she could. She gave him half her own food—and that was only what she got from the neighbors. For this is the custom among the Inuit when someone has made a good catch—to share the food with the village. But the cub grew tall and smart, and in the spring he soon learned to hunt salmon and seal himself, which he brought home to the old woman. The children of the village loved him. They used to play with him and roll and tumble him in the snow like a little white ball.

Soon the old woman had plenty to eat. She fed the cub on great slices of blubber from the fat seals he caught, and they were very happy together.

The old woman was very proud. Now she too could run to the door and call "Come!" to the people of the village, whenever Kunikdjuaq brought home a specially fine seal or salmon.

Kunikdjuaq was a wonderful hunter. He was far more skillful and successful than the grown men of the village. They began to be envious. Their envy grew so big that finally they decided to kill the young bear. The children heard the people talking and ran and told the old woman.

The old woman went to all the houses, one by one, and begged them not to kill her beautiful cub. "Do not kill my son," she said. She begged them to kill her instead. But the people would not listen. They were determined to get rid of Kunikdjuaq. They said he was fat and would make a fine feast for the whole village.

The old woman ran home quickly then and told the young bear that his life was in danger. "Run away," she said. "Run away and don't come back." Then because her heart was breaking, she begged him not to go too far—not so far that she could not find him once in a while, she said.

So Kunikdjuaq went away. The old woman grieved bitterly to see him go. And so did the children of the village.

After a while the old woman again had no food, so she went far out on the sea ice looking for her son. She always called him "my son." Soon she saw him and called his name. He heard her and ran to meet her.

She patted him and looked him over to see if he had been hurt in any fights. But the young bear was fat and strong and sleek and white and glossy. Then the old woman told him she needed food.

Off went Kunikdjuaq and came back in a short time with meat and fish. The old woman cut it up in slices with her knife and gave him many big pieces of the blubber before she carried the meat home.

This went on for many years. And today the Inuit still tell this "story of unbroken love" between the old woman and her bear.

The Songs of the Animals

LONG AGO in the beginning every animal had his own song. One day the animals were dancing and singing together in a house with a pole in the middle that held up the roof.

Bear sang, "I dance in the swamps. The swamps are my dancing place."

Elk sang, "I dance on the mountains. The mountains are my dancing place."

Deer sang, "I run when the people come. I run from the people."

Rabbit came along. Rabbit sang, "Move, pole, or I'll shoot you." He aimed his arrow at the pole that held up the roof. "Move, pole, or I'll shoot you," he sang.

So the pole moved.

At first it moved just a little, and then it moved fast. It moved right along to the end of the house. The house was going to fall down, so everybody ran out. Some grew feathers and flew out and went into the trees and stayed there. The ones that did not get out are the mice and rats and lizards: the ones who still like to live under the house today.

This is a story of the Cowlitz Indians, a tribe of the Coast Salish of the State of Washington. It was a great favorite with children, and sometimes an old person would make a child swim in the river "to pay for the story." No child would be so bad mannered as to fall asleep or ask for anything to eat during the storytelling. This telling is based on a story collected by Thelma Adamson in 1926–1927 and published in her *Folk-Tales of the Coast Salish*.

Atam and Im

IN THE BEGINNING of the world there was a man named Atam and a woman named Im. Chief was in the upper world. His name was God. Outcast was in the lower world. Chief often came into the world and talked to the man and woman and told them what to do.

One day Outcast made a horse and put it on the earth to see what the man and woman would do.

Im looked at the horse and said, "There's God come to visit us."

"Oh, that's not God," said Atam.

But the horse was so beautiful that after a while Atam thought it must be God, and he walked out and spoke to it. When God came along and saw the two people talking to the horse, he said, "Don't talk to the horse. Outcast made it, hoping somehow to harm you." Then God looked at the horse.

"Well, since he is here," he said, "I will fix him for some good purpose." So God licked his two thumbs and pressed them on the beast's front legs, so that he would carry the mark of God's hands and not be just the creature of Outcast.

"Your name is Horse," said God, as he marked the two front

legs. "You shall be a servant and a friend of the people forever."

Soon the mosquitoes began to bite the horse. So God took some long grass and made a long tail for the horse.

"Swish them away, henceforth," he said.

He took some more grass and made a thick mane on the neck of the horse. "Shake it," he said.

Then he threw some in front of the horse. "This is your food," he said. The grass began to grow and soon covered the whole bare earth. And the horse stretched his head down and began to eat it.

Then God said good-by to the man and woman.

"Don't eat any fruit," he said, "until I come back and show you the proper kinds."

All the trees were full of fruit in the beginning; even the pine trees and firs had big juicy fruit. But the man and woman had never eaten any because God had not yet told them which ones were good.

One day Outcast came along, pretending to be God, and gave Im one of the big long fruits of the pine tree.

"Eat it," he said.

So Im ate it and gave some to Atam. Outcast watched them eat it and then ran off. Suddenly all the fruits on the pine trees and firs shriveled up into little cones, and the big fruits on the bushes turned into berries.

When God came along and saw what had happened, he sent Im away to live with Outcast. Then he broke off a piece of Atam's rib and made a new woman to be his wife. After that they had many children, and the world was populated.

This is the way the Thompson River Indians of southern British Columbia told their story about the first man and woman after they had heard the white man tell his. The northwestward spread of the horse from the Plains was slow; and these people probably did not possess horses much before 1840. This retelling is based on the tale as presented by James A. Teit in *Mythology of the Thompson Indians*.

The Acorn Maidens

LONG AGO in the beginning of the world, when the acorns and the animals and the old gods lived together, one day the gods said to the acorns, "Man is being created. He is coming here. Make yourselves nice hats, because you had better go away."

So the acorns began to make themselves hats and little caps.

Black Oak Acorn was very slow, and when the time came to go, she had not finished hers. So she picked up a big bowl-shaped basket with stripes painted on it and turned it over her head for a hat.

Tan Oak Acorn did not have time to clean the straws out from inside hers. When the time came to go, she clapped it on and hurried off, with the straws sticking out. And the straws still stick out of Tan Oak Acorn's little hat today.

Post Oak Acorn finished hers all right and cleaned it well and finished it off, neat and tight and tidy.

So did Maul Oak Acorn. She too made herself a nice, neat, finished little hat.

Then they hurried off to that place where the spirits now dwell.

But one day later, they just let go of the trees they lived in and spilled down into the place where the human beings were. And they turned their faces into their hats as they fell.

Post Oak Acorn and Maul Oak Acorn were proud of their finished hats. They did not think much of Tan Oak Acorn's untidy little cap with the straws sticking out.

So Tan Oak Acorn began to wish.

"I wish that I shall make the best acorn soup of all," she said. She was jealous of Post Oak Acorn and Maul Oak Acorn because of their finished hats. "Let their soups be black and bitter," she wished.

And so it is. The Karok Indians in that place found out that

Post Oak Acorn and Maul Oak Acorn do not taste very good, and the soups made from them are black. Tan Oak Acorn makes the best soup.

Black Oak Acorn still wears the stripes of her upside-down bowl hat. All of them still turn their faces into their hats as they fall to earth. If you pick up an acorn and take off its hat, you can see the little tiny nose on its face.

Ants

AT FIRST there was nothing but water. The great primeval sea stretched everywhere. There was nothing else.

Two brothers who had never opened their eyes because of the stinging salt water lived under the sea. The older brother was named Chaipa-Komat and the younger was Kokomat.

One day Chaipa-Komat rose to the top of the water and opened his eyes and looked around. He saw nothing but water. Soon Kokomat followed his brother to the surface to find out what was going on. But he was impatient; he opened his eyes too soon, and the sharp sea water got into them and blinded him.

"There ought to *be* something," said Chaipa-Komat. So he made a lot of little red ants. Then he made some more little red ants; more and more he made, until they filled up the ocean and thus made the land. Whoever doubts that the earth is made of ants needs only to dig into it—and there they are!

Then Chaipa-Komat made birds, but they flew off in the dark and were lost.

"There ought to be light," he said. So he made a round flat object and tossed it into the sky. This was the moon, and it gave a dim light.

"Not good enough," said Chaipa-Komat, so he made a bigger one. This too he hurled into the sky, and it stayed there, giving off a great bright light. This is the sun. Some people say, however, that Chaipa-Komat spat on his finger and rubbed a big bright spot in the sky to be the sun.

The Center of the World

THE Zuñi Indians have a famous myth called the Emergence myth, telling how the first people climbed up from the underworld to live in the sun on the face of the beautiful earth. They were all living together in one place named Prayerstick Place.

One morning they said, "We are too many. We must separate."

So the people divided themselves and some traveled northward, some west, some south, some east. But there was one lot who said they wanted to live in the middle. They wanted to live in the very center of the world.

"How shall we find the center of the world?" they said.

"I shall find it," said Water Spider.

"Try here," said the people.

So Water Spider laid his heart upon the earth and stretched out his legs to find the rim of the world.

He could touch only two corners. He could touch the corner called East, and he could touch the corner called North. But he could not reach to the west or south.

"This is not the middle," he said.

So Water Spider went searching for a place where his arms could touch the edge of the world in all four directions. And the people went with him.

"I shall measure again at Halona," Water Spider said to them.

So when they came to Halona, Water Spider laid his heart upon the earth and stretched out his arms and legs. He could touch all four corners of the world: north, west, south, east.

"*Here* is the middle of the world," he said, "for I touch the very edge all round. Live here, my people," he said. "Live here forever."

So the people settled at Halona, which is the middle of the world.

"Here you shall not be overthrown," said Water Spider, "for here your hearts will be strong. Here your hearts will not be to one side or the other."

The Zuñi Indians have lived at Halona from that day to this, and Halona is now a district of Zuñi.

Turkey Girl

ONCE there was an old couple living together at San Juan (New Mexico): Shriveled Corn Old Woman and Prayer-stick Old Man. They had two daughters. Yellow Corn Girl was the older, and the younger one was called Turkey Girl because she took care of the turkeys. She took care of the turkeys all the time.

When it came time to go to the great feast and dance of the people, the parents took Yellow Corn Girl with them; but little Turkey Girl stayed home to take care of the turkeys.

"Why don't you go too? You can go," said the turkeys.

"I have no clothes," said Turkey Girl. "I have no moccasins. I have no beads."

"You shall have everything," said the turkeys.

Then Turkey Man shook his wing, and a big black shawl fell out of it. He nudged the next turkey.

The next turkey shook his wing, and a beautiful belt fell out of it. He nudged the next turkey.

The next turkey shook his wing, and there was a pair of lovely moccasins. The next turkey shook his wing, and there lay a white blanket. He nudged the next turkey, and the next turkey produced beads and beads and beads.

Thus Turkey Girl had everything she needed and got ready to go.

She went. She came to the place and arrived before morning, before the dancers came out. So she stood in a corner to watch.

Her sister saw her and said to the mother, "Look! Turkey Girl has come here! Where did she get the clothes?" And they went over and scolded her for leaving home. So Turkey Girl ran home crying.

"Why are you crying?" asked the turkeys.

"They scolded me! They would not let me stay." And Turkey Girl cried and cried.

"I'm going away!" she said. "Somewhere where they will let me *stay!* And I will take you with me, all my dears!"

So they went away, Turkey Girl and her turkeys. After a while they came to a lake.

"Good-by, my children," she said to the turkeys. "Go live in the mountains. I am going to live here."

So the turkeys flew away, north, west, south, east, into the mountains, and Turkey Girl went into the lake.

"There in the mountains have your little ones and live your lives," she called after them. And after that those mountains were full of wild turkeys.

When the father and the mother and the older sister came home from the dance, Turkey Girl was gone and so were all the turkeys. They looked around everywhere, but they never did find them.

This is the Cinderella story of the Tewa Indians of New Mexico, following the telling as presented by Elsie Clews Parsons in her

Tewa Tales. Nobody knows for sure whether the Tewa learned this story from the Spaniards, or whether it is their own. One thing is certain: it is completely Tewa in incident, culture, and emotion.

The Zuñi Indian Cinderella story is a little more recognizable as being related to the European version which is so familiar to all of us. In the Zuñi story, the turkeys provide Turkey Girl with clothes and beads so that she may go to the great tribal dance, but they warn her to come home at a certain hour. She has such a wonderful time, however, that she forgets and stays and stays to watch the dancers. Suddenly she remembers the warning and runs home as fast as she can. But the turkeys have all flown away into the mountains, Turkey Girl's beautiful clothes disappear, and she stands again in rags.

Gluskap

ONE DAY the great creator god of the Micmac Indians made Gluskap to be their special god and culture hero, to fix up their country for them, and teach them how to get along on this earth. He took up a piece of earth and shaped it and breathed upon it, and there was Gluskap. This happened at Cape North on the east shore of Cape Breton Island, Nova Scotia.

So Gluskap went around shaping the country. He traveled all along the shores in his canoe. One day the canoe broke to pieces on some rocks, and Gluskap got out and came ashore. But the canoe is still there: three long narrow islands in a straight line offshore (between St. Ann Bay and Great Bras d'Or) are called Gluskap's Canoe.

Two young girls saw this happen. They saw the canoe break in three pieces and watched the dripping Gluskap wade ashore. They thought he looked awfully funny, and they laughed and laughed. Gluskap heard them making fun of him.

"All right. Stay there and laugh!" he said. So the two girls were instantly changed into two rocks, which are there today. The Indians named this place Twôbutc, Looking Out, for the two girls who looked out and laughed at Gluskap. Today the place is named Plaster Cove.

Gluskap walked on across Cape Breton Island. He sat down and had his dinner on the south side of Great Bras d'Or. That place is now called Padalodi'tck, Table Head. Then he went on across Bras d'Or Lake and stopped at Wísik, Indian Island, in the western end of it.

Here he started a beaver and chased him westward all the way to what is now St. Patrick's Bay. The chase went on; the beaver headed up into the Bay of Fundy. At Pligauk, Split Place, now called Split Point, Gluskap dug out a channel with his paddle to

287

let the water out so he could find the beaver. This is now Minas Basin, on the northwestern shore of Nova Scotia. Here he caught the beaver.

The pot he used to cook the beaver is there today: a little island named Pot Rock, and near it is another tiny island which was Gluskap's dog as he sat near-by sniffing the wonderful odor of beaver for dinner. The water still drains completely out of Minas Basin on every tide. Thus Gluskap caused the huge forty-foot tides that sweep in and out of Minas Basin.

From Minas Basin Gluskap walked eastward to Pictou, where many Micmacs lived. There he taught the Indians all they know: how to make bows and arrows and how to build canoes. He taught them how to hunt and fish and gave them great wisdom.

Then one day Gluskap said to the people, "I am going away now. The white man is coming. You will all be baptized, but I am going where the white man cannot find me." So he departed. "But if you need me, in time of war," he said as he was leaving, "if you need me, call, and I'll come back."

Then Gluskap went away and did not stop until he came to the North Pole. There he sits today, making bows and arrows against the time when the white men might harm the Micmacs. The Micmacs still call themselves Gluskap's children—even the ones who are baptized—and they know that he will come and save them in their time of need.

When Peary discovered the North Pole, there was Gluskap, sitting on top of it—and they spoke to each other.

Fire

A STORY OF THE ALABAMA INDIANS

ONCE long ago the bears owned all the fire in the world. Wherever they went they used to carry it with them. One day they were eating acorns in the forest, and they set the fire on the ground while they were eating. They ate more and more acorns and wandered farther and farther through the woods seeking them. They forgot the fire, and it nearly went out.

"Feed me! Feed me!" cried Fire. But the bears were too far; they did not hear.

A man came along and saw the fire.

"Feed me! Feed me!" cried Fire.

The man picked up a stick and leaned it on the fire to the north. He got another stick to the west and laid it on the fire to the west. He picked up a stick to the south and laid it to the south of the fire. Still another stick he laid on the fire to the east.

Fire blazed up for the man with a bright flickering blaze and made a nice warmth.

When the bears came back looking for their fire, Fire said, "I don't even know you!" It blazed up so hot the bears could not take it.

They never did get it back. Now fire belongs to man.

The Milky Way

LONG AGO, say the Seminole Indians of the Florida Everglades and Cypress Swamp, the creator, whom they call Breathmaker, blew his breath across the sky and made the beautiful white path which leads from the edge of this world to the land of the dead in the west. They call it *solopi heni,* spirit way. We call it the Milky Way. The souls of all good people travel this path, but the souls of the wicked never walk it. The bad ones have to stay in their graves.

The path shines brightest for the souls of the "very good." Who are the very good? You can always tell, say the Seminole, because the very good are always dearly loved; they do not lie; they do not steal; and their speech is kind and never evil. They never get drunk, and they are full of courage. These things are what makes a person very good in the ethics of the Seminole.

The Seminole see another, smaller path in the sky, called *ifi heni,* dog way, which slants up until it joins the spirit path and continues on to the city in the sky where all good dogs and people go. You can see the *ifi heni* on very bright nights. Long ago, when a good man died, the people used to kill his dog so that the two could travel the spirit path together. Once a soul has traveled the spirit path, the Milky Way, it never comes back. The Seminole do not believe that the very good would come back to trouble or frighten the living.

A Chimalteco Story

THE first Chimalteco Indian was named José, and María was his wife. José made the earth, and next he made mankind. The earth was flat, flat, flat, and the people never tired because there were no hills. The whole world was dark. Even José could not see to work, and the people did not know when to sleep and when to wake.

Father José wanted to look at the people, so he made the sun to light the world; then he made the moon to follow the sun around and give the people a little light in the night.

Then Jesús Cristo was born, the first son of José and María. The first day after Jesús Cristo was born, he sat up and told José, "My name is Jesús Cristo." He said that he would fix up the world. "And you, my father, shall help me," he said.

So Jesús Cristo began his work. He made mountains rise up in the flat earth, with valleys between them, and he made *barrancas* (gorges) for the rivers. He made roads over and around the mountains for the Chimalteco to travel.

When the Devil and his people saw the mountains they were enraged. They did not like them.

"That José and his son put them there!" they said. "Let's kill them!"

They began to search for Jesús Cristo. They hunted and searched for twenty days and never found him. They asked the turkeys and chickens if they had seen him, and the turkeys and chickens, those jabbering ones, told them where to look. But the horses and the mules would not tell. So people do not kill or sacrifice horses and mules today. Everybody sacrifices turkeys and chickens, however, on account of that gossiping. The cow was a tattler, too; and so cows get sold for beef.

Jesús fled from the Devil and his people for forty days, and one day when they were getting close he hid in the stomach of a dead horse. The stink of the horse kept them from looking too close, so they went away.

The next day Jesús dug a pit under a palm tree, and when it was deep he walked out of it backwards, so that his footprints showed as if going in but not coming out. Then he climbed up in the palm tree and hid. When the searchers came along, they rushed into the pit, following the footprints, and Jesús came down from the tree and quietly filled up the pit and covered them.

At the end of forty days the Devil's crowd caught up with Jesús Cristo. They made a cross and crucified him, and made a blind man kill him with a knife. This was a great kindness, because it ended the suffering of Jesús. So today the blind walk everywhere unharmed, and people are kind to them.

Then they laid the body of Jesús Cristo down at the edge of the pueblo (village). And in the middle of the night a little burro came along and breathed upon it. The wounds from the nails were thus quickly healed, and Jesús got up and went to heaven.

The next day when the people of the Devil came along, they were frightened when they found that the body had disappeared. They asked the neighbors where Jesús was, and the people said, "He has gone to heaven."

Then the people of the Devil were terrified indeed and hid behind trees. But thunder and lightning came and destroyed them all.

The Eternal Wanderer

THE Miskito Indians of northeastern Honduras and eastern Nicaragua have a story about a little boy who lived long ago with his people on the banks of Río Patuca. They call him Tismila.

He was always a very hungry little boy, and he used to put his hand in his mother's cooking pot when she wasn't looking and pick out all the best pieces of meat for himself and eat them before the others had a chance. When mealtime came there would be nothing left for the others but cassava and some bananas baking in the hearth ashes.

His mother scolded him for this, and his father scolded him. But he would not listen. The Miskito Indians are very lenient with children and never punish them. They seem to feel that a child can learn by being told the difference between right and wrong, and that the gods themselves will take care of disobedience.

So the father and the mother scolded this child for eating the meat before mealtime and depriving the family. But he would not listen. His grandmother tried to teach him better, and his older brother made fun of him for greediness. But nothing cured him. In two or three days he would do it again.

One day when the little boy put his hand in the cooking pot to take the meat, the pot closed up the minute he got his hand inside it. He could not pull it out. He tried and tried, but the pot had closed tight around his wrist, and nothing he could do would pull it free.

He banged the pot on the ground, but it would not break. He ran out of the house and banged it against a tree, but it would not break. And he never did get it off.

Now that little boy is an old, old man. He wanders through the forests, banging the pot desperately against the trees. But nothing ever breaks it.

Sometimes at night the Miskito Indians can hear him. The sound of the pot against the tree makes a thunderous noise. Sometimes it comes nearer; sometimes it recedes. And when the Miskito hear it, they say, "There goes the Wandering One. There goes Tismila." They explain that he will have to wander forever like that, poor fellow.

León and the Lion

THERE is a little village sitting on the edge of a jungle somewhere in the world, where the people live very happily most of the time. But one day not long ago, a big lion came walking into the village and ate a man.

He went away then, but a few days later he came back and ate two men. About a week later he came walking into the village and ate three men.

So three of the bravest hunters went into the jungle to hunt the lion. But they never came back. Nobody ever found out what happened.

More hunters went into the jungle to hunt the lion—and they never came back.

This happened several times, and at last the people of the village were afraid to go hunting for the lion. And the lion kept coming into the village and eating the people.

At last the king sent a messenger through all the world for somebody to please come and kill the lion.

First came some Englishmen. They wore short pants and sun helmets; and the first thing they did was sit down and make tea. While they were drinking the tea, the lion came and ate them.

Next came some Germans. They knew all about lions from studying in books, and they had made a map showing just how they were going to hunt this lion and catch it.

But while they were studying the map, the lion came and ate them.

Next came some Frenchmen. They were very polite. One of them saw the lion and pointed his gun at it, then suddenly remembered his manners.

"After you!" he said, and bowed to his companion.

"Oh, no! After you!" said the other fellow. And while they were bowing to each other, the lion came and ate them.

Next came some Americans. They had wonderful big guns. But while they were polishing and oiling the guns, the lion came and ate them, too.

Then a young Mexican boy came along. He was very young and very handsome. His name was León (*león* means lion in Spanish).

The first thing he did was lean a big convex mirror up against a tree at the edge of the forest. The lion came along and saw himself in it. He thought, Oh, what a big fierce lion I am! So he went into the village and ate four people.

The king was very angry. He thought that León had just made matters worse.

"Just wait, your majesty. Just wait," León begged.

The next day León leaned another mirror against the tree. This one was not quite so big, not quite so convex as the first one. The lion didn't look quite so big to himself. That day he ate only two people.

The next day León put a flat mirror against the tree. When the lion looked at himself, he thought he looked like just any old lion, so that day he ate only one silly old woman.

The next day León put up a smaller mirror—a little bit concave.

When the lion came along and looked, he saw a fairly small lion in there. That day he just stood on the edge of the village and didn't feel very hungry.

The next day León's mirror was smaller yet, and more concave. When the lion saw himself in it, he felt so insignificant that he just slunk back into the jungle.

The next day León leaned a very small mirror against the tree —a tiny mirror, very concave.

When the lion looked into it he saw such a *little* lion that he thought he was a kitten! Then León came along and put him in a paper bag and took him to the king.

The king and the people of the village were so happy that they had a big feast that night, and León went home to Mexico with lots of money.

The Armadillos

ONCE upon a time the Lightnings decided they would strike the earth and kill all the Armadillos. But the Armadillos heard about the plan and prayed to the god Maluime for some way of escape. "Remove the strength from them," said Maluime. "Make them laugh."

So when the Lightnings arrived on earth, there were the Armadillos—expecting them. There were the Armadillos walking up and down in ridiculous antics.

The Lightnings laughed. The Armadillos walked up and down

some more. They curled their tails, and uncurled them. They jumped around. Some of them pulled into their shells and rolled up, and the others used them for footballs. When they got tired of that, they did some more crazy things.

The Lightnings laughed so hard they cried. Tears streamed down them from laughing. And the ground was so wet from their tears that the worms came crawling up out of the earth into daylight. So instead of killing the Armadillos as they had originally intended, the Lightnings picked up worms and fed them to the Armadillos.

Even today worms are the favorite food of the Armadillos. And the Taulipang Indians of Guiana now have a magic charm to make an enemy laugh. The words of the charm mention the Armadillos, in memory of this great event.

A Catío Indian Legend
About Themselves

WHEN God first created the world the Catío Indians were not fools or beasts. They had great wisdom. The reason they are fools now, they say, is because a Catío woman made a grave mistake long ago.

Once in those early days of the world, when all was good, a *birrí* came and wooed a young Catío woman. (A *birrí* is a very poisonous serpent of that region.) The *birrí* wooed the girl and finally she married him, but she did not dare to tell her father.

She hid her serpent husband under a big pile of firewood at the foot of a tree, and as the firewood decreased from being used in the house, she brought more and piled it high, so that he could live there safely without being seen.

Time passed and the young girl gave birth to a little serpent son, whom she also hid under the woodpile with his father. One day the serpent grandmother came with a great troop of attendants to see her grandchild, and very soon after the serpents had gone, the girl's father came home.

"I smell *birrí!*" he said, and began hunting all over. The odor of *birrí* was strong around the place, for so many of them had been there.

He smelled and he searched, and finally he found the serpent husband and the little serpent grandson under the pile of wood. He did not ask any questions, for he understood the situation at once.

He was furious with his daughter. He killed the *birrí* husband and the little *birrí* child.

The serpent grandmother rushed back to revive her son, but when she got the body pieced together, it turned into a Spaniard.

The Spaniard was full of hatred for the Indians and made war on them, and they fled from his soldiers into the mountains.

Here in their isolation they became fools, the Catío say. But they wish to remain as they are. If they should become people again, they say, the serpent-Spaniards would return and annihilate them.

Fire

A STORY OF THE TOBA INDIANS

THE Owner of Fire among the Toba Indians of the Argentine Chaco was an old, old woman. She was very stingy with her fire. She would neither lend it nor give any away, not even a little small spark. So the carancho birds decided to get some.

The carancho is a kind of hawk in that country, and the people admire him very much for his wisdom and his patience.

One day the caranchos went to visit the old Owner of Fire. She was asleep, and so they waited till she woke up.

"Grandmother, give us a brand," they said. But she would not.

"Grandmother, give us one small burning twig." But she would not.

So the caranchos sat around waiting for her to go to sleep again. After a while she did, and then one of the caranchos picked up a glowing coal in his claw and flew away. All the others flew off with him to help. First one would carry it, then another.

The old fire woman woke up and chased after them, but she never caught them. She had to go back.

The caranchos flew into the forest and hid the fire in the trees. There is fire in every tree, the Toba say. And so when they want to make fire, they rub two sticks of wood together and let it out.

Milomaki

MILOMAKI was a lovely boy who suddenly came walking among the Yahuna people one day and began to sing. The people had never seen him before. It just happened that one day Milomaki came walking out of the east—and there he was.

When the boy sang the people dropped their work and came running to hear him. And the song was so beautiful that they forgot everything.

That night after they had eaten their evening meal, all those who had listened fell dead. The relatives of the dead were full of fear and resentment against the strange singer, because they thought he had caused the deaths. So they caught and killed him and burned his young body on a high pyre.

From his ashes grew the paxiuba palm tree, and Milomaki himself flew into the sky. After a while the people learned to use and love the paxiuba palm. They learned that the bark was good for bedding and to cover walls. They used the trunk of the tree to make canoes; and they used the paxiuba wood to make their hunting bows. Best of all, the Yahuna learned to make the big paxiuba flutes which sang the same wonderful songs which Milomaki had sung to the people.

The Yahuna Indians love and honor these big flutes and keep them safely hidden most of the time. But once every year the men bring them out and play them in the thanksgiving festival for the harvest of fruits. And at this time they dance in honor of Milomaki, whom they now regard as the benefactor of mankind.

Sun and Moon

FAR to the south, off the southern tip of South America, at the end of the world, lies the bitter-cold land of fire, Tierra del Fuego. It was named by Ferdinand Magellan, as he sailed along its coasts in 1520, because from the ship it looked to him as if the shores were lined with fire—and they were.

Every family in that icy land had its own fire in front of its own dwelling. The Ona Indians of Tierra del Fuego lived at that time in semicircular windbreak shelters made of guanaco skins stretched and slanted between two upright poles. The guanaco hides were sewed together and painted red, and a little earth was scooped away inside the semicircle to make a hollow place which was laid with branches. This was the Ona house: open on one side—but here was the family fire, protected from the wind by the scarlet wind screen and throwing back its blazing warmth against the embracing wall.

303

If there was any wood available, the Ona sometimes made cone-shaped tepees with sapling framework and a cover of branches. But still the great fire always burned before the opening.

The Ona Indians tell a story about the sun and moon which explains the markings on the moon's face. Long ago Sun and Moon were husband and wife. But one day they quarreled and fought, and Sun pinched Moon's face so hard that the marks still show today. They are still mad and can still be seen chasing each other in circles around the sky.

But Sun never catches Moon. As he gets nearer and nearer, Moon gets smaller and smaller, and then, one night, she cannot be seen at all. Sun goes on by. But after he has passed, there is Moon again, very little and thin at first, but growing larger and larger night by night, until her whole face can once again be seen.

The Ona say that when Moon is thin, thin, thin, she is ravenously hungry and will come to earth and eat bad children. So, at the time of the new moon, mothers keep their children indoors. And when the moon is fat again, the children run outdoors chanting,

> The moon is fat,
> The moon has eaten,
> But she did not eat me,
> She did not eat me.

Author's Notes

YOU'VE HEARD ABOUT...

Paul Bunyan. This story of Paul Bunyan includes only motifs authenticated as originating in oral tradition among the old-time loggers; and of these only a few are given. All are based on material presented by Daniel G. Hoffman in *Paul Bunyan, Last of the Frontier Demigods.* For statements in reference to pre-Paul logging tales, see p. 165, note 2.

Pecos Bill. This story is based on E. A. O'Reilly's "The Saga of Pecos Bill" in *Century Magazine* (October, 1923) reprinted in B. A. Botkin's *A Treasury of American Folklore,* pp. 180–185, and on the selection from M. C. Boatright's *Tall Tales from Texas,* Dallas, 1934, reprinted in B. A. Botkin's *A Treasury of Western Folklore,* pp. 674–676.

Johnny Appleseed. All the information in this article is gleaned from Robert Price's definitive book, *Johnny Appleseed, Man and Myth.*

John Henry. This story is based on tales from L. W. Chappel's *John Henry, A Folk-Lore Study* presented in B. A. Botkin's *A Treasury of American Folklore,* pp. 233–234, and on the John Henry ballad from John A. and Alan Lomax's *American Ballads and Folk Songs* presented by Dr. Botkin on pp. 235–239. The lines from the hammer songs as given here are based on those collected in Kentucky by E. C. Perrow and included in his "Songs and Rhymes from the South" in the *Journal of American Folklore,* Vol. 26, pp. 163, 164 (1913).

Daniel's Dear. This episode is retold from Charles McKnight's *Our Western Border* (Philadelphia, 1876), reprinted in B. A. Botkin's *A Treasury of Southern Folklore,* p. 162.

Davy Crockett. Davy's introductory speech to Congress is quoted from *Sketches and Eccentricities of Colonel David Crockett of West Tennessee* (London, 1836).

Mike Fink. The description of the keelboats and river fights in this story is based on material in Herbert Asbury's *The French Quarter,* pp. 49, 50, 52, and 53. Statements about the Carpenter episode are based on "The Western Boatmen" in Henry Howe's *The Great West,* Vol. 2, pp. 234ff. And the story of the shooting match between Mike and Davy Crockett is based on material from one of the Crockett almanacs in B. A. Botkin's *A Treasury of American Folklore,* pp. 7–8. The item about bringing Mike Fink's body back to Pennsylvania is from an article by Henry W. Shoemaker in the Harrisburg *Capital News,* January 6, 1956.

Annie Christmas. This article is based on the story as told in Herbert Asbury's *The French Quarter* and Carl Carmer's *The Hurricane's Children.*

Casey Jones. This telling of the Casey Jones legend is based on B. A. Botkin's *A Treasury of American Folklore,* pp. 241–245, citing the *Erie Railroad Magazine,* Vol. 24, pp. 13, 44 (1928) and Vol. 28, pp. 12, 46 (1932). B. McKeown's "Casey Jones" in *Yankee,* Vol. 19, pp. 38ff. (May, 1955) and Malcolm Laws' *Native American Balladry,* pp. 204–205, were also used.

STATE LORE

Idaho. The analysis of the Indian word *ee-da-how* is that given by John E. Rees in "Idaho: Its Meaning, Origin, and Application," in the *Oregon Historical Quarterly,* Vol. 18, p. 4 (1917).

Indiana. The anecdote about the liars' bench is from *Hoosier Tall Stories,* Federal Writers' Project, 1937.

Kansas. The giant cornstalk is a familiar of the Western tall tale. In some versions it is the farmer himself who climbs the stalk to inspect the crop. Some versions say that the boy (or man) was rescued by a balloonist; some say that the kind-hearted farmer (or neighbors) shot him to keep him from starving to death. This particular tale is based on one published in the *Herald Leader and Democrat* of Menominee, Michigan, in 1905, and presented by Richard M. Dorson in *Western Folklore,* Vol. 6, p. 180 (1947).

Kentucky. The meanings of the phrases "to drive a nail" and "to snuff the candle" are taken from John James Audubon's "Kentucky Sports," *Ornithological Biography,* Vol. 1 (Philadelphia, 1831); reference is in Henry Howe's *The Great West,* Vol. 2, p. 231.

Massachusetts. The big take of codfish for which Cape Cod is named is recorded in "The Relation of Captain Gosnolf's Voyage, 1602" in *Purchas His Pilgrimes,* 1625 (cited by B. A. Botkin in *A Treasury of New England Folklore,* p. 431).

Michigan. The information about Beaver Island is from I. H. Walton's article "Folk Singing on Beaver Island," *Midwest Folklore,* Vol. 2, pp. 243ff.

Mississippi. The mosquito story is based on Ruth E. Bass's Mississippi tall tale "Big Skeeters" in B. A. Botkin's *A Treasury of Southern Folklore,* p. 461.

Nevada. The anecdote about the Nevada sinks is based on the telling of it in Dan De Quille's *History of the Big Bonanza* (American Publishing Company, Hartford, Conn., 1876).

Ohio. Ohio has not been very busy collecting its folk beliefs and sayings. But an Ohio Folklore Archive was established at Miami University, Oxford, Ohio, in 1948; so there is hope that Ohio lore will not be entirely lost and forgotten.

Oklahoma. The material for the Cheyenne story was contributed by Charles N. Gould to B. A. Botkin's *Folk-Say, A Regional Miscellany,* 1930, pp. 65–66.

Oregon. The terms and definitions of logger lingo are taken from W. A. Davis' "Logger and Splinter-Picker Talk," in *Western Folklore,* Vol. 9, pp. 115, 116, 118, 121.

Pennsylvania. The comments in this article on Pennsylvania folk heroes, coal mines, and mining songs are based on material in George Korson's *Pennsylvania Songs and Legends.*

Rhode Island. The story of the *Palatine* is based on the telling in C. M. Skinner's *Myths and Legends of Our Own Land*, pp. 48–50. The enumeration of the few Rhode Island tall tales is taken from Richard M. Dorson's "Jonny-Cake Papers" in the *Journal of American Folklore*, Vol. 58, pp. 104ff.

Texas. The cowboy material in this article is based on John A. and Alan Lomax's *Cowboy Songs and Other Frontier Ballads.*

Utah. The mining anecdotes are based on the material in Wayland D. Hand's "Folklore from Utah's Silver Mining Camps," in the *Journal of American Folklore*, Vol. 54, pp. 135ff. The cricket legends are based on G. E. Shankle's *State Names, Flags, Seals . . . etc.*, pp. 350, 386; and B. H. Roberts' *Comprehensive History of the Church of Jesus Christ of Latter Saints*, Vol. 3 (Salt Lake City), in B. A. Botkin's *A Treasury of Western Folklore*, pp. 687–688.

Vermont. The anecdote about the two young men is based on the telling of it in Charles M. Skinner's *Myths and Legends of Our Own Land*, Vol. 1, pp. 223–224.

Virginia. The telling of the dog-cat story is based on the version presented by A. N. Bacon and E. C. Parsons in the collection entitled "Folklore from Elizabeth City County, Virginia," in the *Journal of American Folklore*, Vol. 35, p. 279, No. 33 (1922).

Washington. The Coyote story is based on one of the Columbia River origin tales in James A. Teit's collection of Okanagon tales in *Folk-Tales of Salishan and Sahaptin Tribes*, edited by Franz Boas. The Asa Mercer episode is based on Nancy W. Ross's *Westward the Women* (New York, 1944), presented in B. A. Botkin's *A Treasury of Western Folklore*, pp. 592ff.

BAD MEN

Jesse James. This story of Jesse James is the one told in many books. The anecdote of Anne Limrick's watch is based on the report of Mrs. Ivah M. Shallenberger (granddaughter of Anne Limrick) in the *New Mexico Folklore Record*, Vol. 2, p. 40 (1947).

Stackalee. This story is a composite of the article "Stackalee" by B. A. Botkin in the *Dictionary of Folklore, Mythology, and Legend*, and the tale as told by O. L. Spencer in *Direction*, Vol. 4, pp. 14–17 (1941) and presented by B. A. Botkin in *A Treasury of American Folklore*, pp. 122ff.

TALL TALK

The Shaggy Dog. This version is a very condensed outline of the prolonged and detailed account of dog after dog after dog being found, presented, and rejected by the woman as not shaggy enough, remembered from several oral tellings.

Author's Notes

STRANGE TALES

The Big Black Umbrella. This story was told to John Bennett by Mary Simmons herself, and he has seen the umbrella. This retelling is based, with his permission, on his story "The Remember Service" in his *Doctor to the Dead.*

SCREAMS

Oh, Deary Me. I first heard this story in Indiana in a group of college girls sitting together in a circle by candlelight, deliciously disobeying the lights-out rule. But where the narrator hailed from I do not remember.

   A North Carolina version of the tale was collected by Dr. Ralph Steele Boggs and published in the *Journal of American Folklore,* Vol. 47, p. 297 (1934). In this telling the old woman screams and runs out of the house. No point is made of the dramatic scream of the teller. Dr. Boggs classifies the North Carolina story in the type of European folk tale featuring the fearless hero who encounters dismembered bodies which reassemble, sleeps under a dead man on a gallows, and plays cards with ghosts, all blithely and without fear. This old woman, however, seems hardly to fit into the fearless heroine picture. This tale seems rather to belong to a distinct group, along with "Miss Jenny Jones," in which the main character, the listeners, and teller are all scared to death.

Miss Jenny Jones. This is a very old game played everywhere (with slight variations) in the British Isles, and represents the very ancient belief that excessive grieving disturbs the rest of the dead and causes the spirit to rise. Alice B. Gomme gives seventeen full versions of this as played in England, Scotland, and Ireland.

   In this form I have seen and heard this game played on Philadelphia city playgrounds and in Indiana and Pennsylvania play-party groups.

Shall I Be So? This scream is written from memory from one of the college midnight sessions. E. C. Perrow gives versions of the chant depicting the same situation but lacking the grim details and ending with "Boo!" to startle the audience.

   In her *Folk Songs of Old New England,* Eloise H. Hubbard reports the "Old Woman All Skin and Bone" as a singing game in which one child plays the corpse and rises with a scream to chase the inquisitive mourners at her grave side.

LOCAL LEGENDS AND POPULAR TALES

Lovers' Leaps. The information about lovers' leaps in Texas is reported in J. Frank Dobie's *Legends of Texas;* the story of the Maiden's Leap in Nebraska is from Louise Pound's "Nebraska Legends of Lovers' Leaps," in *Western Folklore,* Vol. 8, p. 311.

Humbug. This information was given in the Berkeley, California *Daily Gazette,* August 4, 1947, and reprinted in *Western Folklore,* Vol. 6, p. 384 (1947).

The Phantom Ship of the Hudson. This story is retold from Skinner's *Myths and Legends of Our Own Land,* Vol. 1, p. 49.

The Lincoln Totem Pole. This story is based on material in Marius Barbeau's *Totem Poles,* Vol. 1, pp. 402–405, which quotes in part V. C. Eifert's article "Lincoln on a Totem Pole," in *Natural History* (February, 1947).

Jean Sot. These episodes are retold partly from Calvin Claudel's analysis of the cycle in *Southern Folklore Quarterly,* Vol. 8, pp. 297ff. (1944) and Vol. 12, pp. 151ff. (1948).

Why Lizard Can't Sit. This story is based on a Mississippi Negro folk tale, told to Dr. N. N. Puckett, and published in his *Folk Beliefs of the Southern Negro,* p. 559.

Never Mind Them Watermelons. This is a Southern Negro ghost story told all over the South from Alabama eastward and northward to Virginia, Philadelphia, and New York. This version from Alabama is based on a tale collected by A. H. Fauset and published in his "Negro Folk Tales from the South," in the *Journal of American Folklore,* Vol. 40, p. 259.

Twist-mouth Family. Dr. Stith Thompson lists the wry-mouth family as motif X131 in his *Motif-Index of Folk-Literature* (Indiana University Studies 96–112) Bloomington, 1932–1936. He cites a Danish source for it: an unpublished manuscript in the Danske Folkemindesamling (the archives of Danish folk tales, music, songs, dances, customs) in the Royal Library in Copenhagen, and says he has heard the tale in this country only in Kentucky. Clifton Johnson in the *Journal of American Folklore,* Vol. 18, pp. 322–323 (1905) gives it the title of the *Twist-Mouth Family* and says that it hails from Plymouth, Massachusetts. B. A. Botkin includes the Johnson version in his *A Treasury of American Folklore,* and classifies it as a nursery story.

It seems to me inevitable that this folk tale came to America with our ancestors from the British Isles. Its appearance in Nova Scotia, Massachusetts, and Kentucky points to that provenience.

Young Charlotte. This version of the story of Charlotte is based on the New York text given by Fern Bishop in "Songs My Grandmother Sang," in the *Journal of American Folklore,* Vol. 48, pp. 379–381 (1935). And grandmother remembered the night it happened—in Jefferson County, New York.

"Young Charlotte" is the popular title of an American ballad written by Seba Smith in 1840 and published in a little paper called *The Rover* in December, 1843, under the title, "A Corpse Going to a Ball." Seba Smith did not know young Charlotte, or Charlie, or the parents. He read a little news item in the New York *Observer* on February 8, 1840, which presented the bare incident as having happened that New Year's Eve. From this little five-line scrap he wrote the ballad.

Information regarding the spread of the ballad is based on the findings of Malcolm Laws in *Native American Balladry,* pp. 61, 214–215.

The Big Warm Dog. This story is based on the tale contributed by Edith C. Blake to Mrs. Guy E. Speare's *More New Hampshire Folk Tales,* pp. 113ff.

Caldera Dick. "There were other notoriously great and savage whales, whose reputations were enlarged wherever whalemen got together for a gam: Mocha Dick and Galera Dick, whose names were derived from the regions in which they were usually encountered—the seas around the island of Mocha, off the southern coast of Chile, and the seas off Galera, a little cape on the coast of Peru. It seems likely that Melville heard the stories about all three Dicks, for he was whaling in those parts in the year 1841. And I suspect that he turned them all to whatever purpose suited his imaginative mind. The probable inspiration for *Moby Dick,* however, was the sinking of the whaleship *Essex,* rammed and sunk by a sperm whale in mid-Pacific in the year 1820.

"Of the three Dicks, Mocha Dick, at least, was often described as white, or as having a great white scar. Since Melville made his Moby Dick a white whale, perhaps the island of Mocha may rise and take a bow in claim of literary honors. I do not remember my grandfather describing Caldera Dick as white, and the references available to me about Galera Dick are vague in detail, describing him only as a great legendary rogue whale. But whether the Dick was white or black, his legend persisted through the life of the sperm-whale fishery. The name was always Dick, however, whether Mocha, Galera, or Caldera claimed him. And if Caldera Dick was taken, as my grandfather says, 'long before my time,' he was supplanted by Mocha Dick or by Galera Dick, for whalemen kept the story alive and current.

"Perhaps there were three whales. Perhaps the three were one, with three names. Perhaps they were *all* whales—all whales, that is, with the gumption, courage, and honor to fight for their lives and turn upon their hunters. The prowess laid to these legendary whales was often encountered in whales to which no legend was attached. Countless whales smashed the boats of their pursuers, thrashed madly in the wreckage, and escaped, leaving death and destruction behind them. At the time, the crew would probably consider the matter all in the day's work, thanking God that such work did not occur every day. But, next voyage, in a new ship, with green hands to impress—well, what old whaleman would admit to defeat by any run-of-the-mill whale? Only the whale of whales, Caldera Dick, or Galera Dick, or a white whale named Mocha Dick, beyond taking by mortal man, could get the best of *them.*"—Benjamin D. Doane.

Black Bartelmy. This story is based on two anonymous ballads, "The Ballad of the Cape" and "The Ghost on the Roaring Bull," printed and sold in folder form in Yarmouth, Nova Scotia, as a souvenir of Cape Forchu.

OTHER AMERICAN FOLK TALES

Kunikdjuaq, A Bear Story of the Inuit. This tale is based on the story as reported by Franz Boas in *The Central Eskimo,* pp. 638–639.

The Acorn Maidens. This story of the Karok Indians of northwestern California is based on the text as given in John P. Harrington's *Karok Indian Myths,* Bureau of American Ethnology Bulletin 107, pp. 5–7 (1932).

Ants. This is an old story of the Diegueño Indians of southern California, based on material in A. L. Kroeber's *Handbook of the Indians of California,* p. 789.

Author's Notes

The Center of the World. This story is based on the episode of finding the center of the world as told in Ruth Benedict's *Zuñi Mythology*, Vol. 1, pp. 5–6.

Gluskap. This is a Micmac Indian story, told to Dr. Frank G. Speck in the summer of 1914 by John Joe, a Micmac Indian then living at Wycogamagh, Cape Breton Island, Nova Scotia. This retelling is based on the tale as published by him in "Some Micmac Tales from Cape Breton Island," in the *Journal of American Folklore,* Vol. 28, pp. 59–60.

Fire, A Story of the Alabama Indians. This is a story based on the text given in John R. Swanton's *Myths and Tales of the Southeastern Indians,* p. 122.

The Milky Way. This story is based on the ethnographical notes of R. F. Greenlee, published in his article "Folktales of the Florida Seminole," in the *Journal of American Folklore,* Vol. 58, pp. 138–139.

A Chimalteco Story. This is the acculturated creation-plus-crucifixion story of the Chimalteco Indians, living in Santiago Chimaltenango, a little municipality in the mountains of northwestern Guatemala. Their own language is Mam. To the Chimalteco, Jesús Cristo is a local hero. They believe that he created the mountains they live in. He is their god and their ancestor, the first Chimalteco Indian. Was he not crucified at their own *calvario* in Chimaltenango? His character is a vivid syncretism of their own ancient mythological clever trickster-culture-hero and the Christian Jesus. And today Jesús Cristo "lives in the church."

This story is based on that told to Charles Wagley by his informant Diego Martín in Chimaltenango, and published in his monograph *Social and Religious Life of a Guatemalan Village,* pp. 51–52.

The Eternal Wanderer. This telling is based on the outline of this folk tale as presented by Eduard Conzemius in his *Ethnographical Survey of the Miskito and Sumu Indians of Honduras and Nicaragua,* p. 165.

León and the Lion. This story is adapted from a folk tale collected by Octavio Romano in Mexico City and reported in the *New Mexico Folklore Record,* Vol. 6, p. 25.

A Catío Indian Legend. This is the origin legend of the Catío Indians of the Cauca River valley, Colombia, adapted and rewritten from the tale as given by Madre Laura de Santa Catalina in her *Cartas Misionals,* 1936, and reproduced by Gregorio Hernández de Alba in his "Sub-Andean Tribes of the Cauca Valley," in *Handbook of South American Indians,* Vol. 4, p. 326. These Indians, pressed by white colonizers, had fled from their mountains into the jungles of the Sinu River, and thus explained their condition.

Fire, A Story of the Toba Indians. This story is based on the incident as presented by Alfred Métraux in *Myths of the Toba and Pilagá Indians of the Gran Chaco,* p. 109.

Milomaki. This is a culture-hero tale of the Yahuna Indians of the tropical forests of northwestern Brazil, based on the material presented in Robert H. Lowie's "The Tropical Forests," in the *Handbook of South American Indians,* Vol. 3, p. 46.

Sun and Moon. This story is based on the sun and moon myth as reported by John M. Cooper in his article "The Ona" in the *Handbook of South American Indians,* Vol. 1, p. 124.

Bibliography

Adamson, Thelma, *Folk-Tales of the Coast Salish.* Memoir 27, American Folklore Society, 1934, p. 193.

Asbury, Herbert, *The French Quarter.* New York, Pocket Books, Inc., 1949.

Ballad of the Cape. Souvenir folder of Cape Forchu, Yarmouth, Nova Scotia, 1954.

Barbeau, Marius, *Totem Poles,* Vol. 1. National Museum of Canada Bulletin 119, 1950, pp. 402–405.

Benedict, Ruth, *Zuñi Mythology,* Vol. 1. New York, Columbia University Press, 1935, pp. 5–6.

Bennett, John, *The Doctor to the Dead.* New York, Rinehart & Company, Inc., 1947.

Bennett, Wendell C., "Habitations," *Handbook of South American Indians.* Bureau of American Ethnology Bulletin 143, Vol. 5. Washington, 1949, pp. 1–20.

Bergen, Fanny, *Animal and Plant Lore.* Memoir 7, American Folklore Society, 1899, pp. 12, 23, 25, 59, 99.

Boas, Franz, *The Central Eskimo.* Bureau of American Ethnology Report 6, Washington, 1884–1885.

———, *Folk-Tales of Salishan and Sahaptin Tribes.* Memoir 11, American Folklore Society, 1917.

Botkin, B. A., *A Treasury of American Folklore,* New York, Crown Publishers, Inc., 1944.

———, *Folk-Say, A Regional Miscellany.* Norman, University of Oklahoma Press, 1930.

———, *A Treasury of New England Folklore.* New York, Crown Publishers, Inc., 1947.

———, *A Treasury of Southern Folklore.* New York, Crown Publishers, Inc., 1949.

———, *A Treasury of Western Folklore.* New York, Crown Publishers, Inc., 1951.

Frank C. Brown Collection of North Carolina Folklore, Vol. 1, ed. by Paul G. Brewster, Archer Taylor, B. J. Whiting, George P. Wilson, Stith Thompson. Durham, Duke University Press, 1952.

Brown, L. W., "New Mexico Sheepherders' Lore," in B. A. Botkin, *A Treasury of Western Folklore,* p. 535.

Burns, W. N., *The Saga of Billy the Kid.* Garden City, Doubleday, Page & Co., 1926.

Carmer, Carl, *Stars Fell on Alabama.* New York, Farrar & Rinehart, Inc., 1934.

———, *The Hurricane's Children.* New York, Farrar & Rinehart, Inc., 1937.

Conzemius, Eduard, *Ethnographical Survey of the Miskito and Sumu Indians of Honduras and Nicaragua.* Bureau of American Ethnology Bulletin 106, Washington, 1932, p. 165.

Cooper, John M., "The Ona," *Handbook of South American Indians.* Bureau of American Ethnology Bulletin 143, Vol. 1. Washington, 1946, p. 124.

Cox, William T., *Fearsome Creatures of the Lumberwoods.* Washington, 1910.

Davis, Henry C., "Negro Folklore from South Carolina." *Journal of American Folklore,* Vol. 27 (1914), pp. 241ff.

Davis, Wilbur A., "Logger and Splinter-Picker Talk." *Western Folklore,* Vol. 9 (1950), pp. 115, 116, 118, 121.

Dobie, J. Frank, "Bowie and the Bowie Knife." *Southwest Review* (April, 1931).

———, *Legends of Texas.* Publications of the Texas Folk-lore Society 3, 1924.

Bibliography

Doerflinger, William M., *Shantymen and Shantyboys: Songs of the Sailor and Lumberman.* New York, The Macmillan Co., 1951.

Dorson, Richard M., "The Jonny-Cake Papers." *Journal of American Folklore,* Vol. 58 (1945), pp. 104–112.

Earle, Alice Morse, *Child Life in Colonial Days.* New York, The Macmillan Co., 1899.

Farish, Thomas Edwin, *History of Arizona,* 8 vols. Phoenix, 1915–1918.

Fauset, A. H., "Negro Folk Tales from the South." *Journal of American Folklore,* Vol. 40 (1927), p. 259.

Fulton, Maurice G., "Billy, the Kid in Life and Books." *New Mexico Folklore Record,* Vol. 4 (1949–1950), pp. 1ff.

The Galaxy of Wit: or Laughing Philosopher. Boston, 1826.

Gomme, Alice B., *The Traditional Games of England, Scotland, and Ireland,* Vol. 1. London, David Nutt, 1894, pp. 260–283; Vol. 2, 1898.

Goodall, C. L., *Black Tavern Tales.* Brooklyn, N. Y., 1932, p. 82.

Greenlee, R. F., "Folktales of the Florida Seminole." *Journal of American Folklore,* Vol. 58 (1945), pp. 138–139.

Gumbo Ya-Ya: A Collection of Louisiana Folk Tales, by Lyle Saxon, Robert Tallant, and Edward Dreyer. WPA Louisiana Writers' Project, Boston, Houghton Mifflin Co., 1945.

Gunther, John, *Inside U.S.A.* New York, Harper & Brothers, 1947.

Hand, Wayland D., "Folklore from Utah's Silver Mining Camps." *Journal of American Folklore,* Vol. 54 (1941), pp. 135ff.

Harrington, John P., *Karok Indian Myths.* Bureau of American Ethnology Bulletin 107, Washington, 1932, pp. 5–7.

Harris, J. W., "The Humorous Yarn in Early Illinois." *Midwest Folklore,* Vol. 2 (1952), p. 168.

Hernández de Alba, Gregorio, "Sub-Andean Tribes of the Cauca Valley," *Handbook of South American Indians.* Bureau of American Ethnology Bulletin 143, Vol. 4, Washington, 1948, p. 326.

Hodge, Frederick W., *Handbook of American Indians North of Mexico.* Bureau of American Ethnology Bulletin 30, 2 vols., Washington, 1907–1910.

Hoffman, Daniel G., *Paul Bunyan, Last of the Frontier Demigods.* Philadelphia, University of Pennsylvania Press, 1952.

Howe, Henry, *Historical Collections of the Great West,* 2 vols. Cincinnati, 1855.

Hurston, Zora Neale, *Mules and Men.* Philadelphia, J. B. Lippincott Co., 1935.

Irving, Washington, *Tales of a Traveller.* 1824.

Ives, Roland L., "Folklore of Eastern Park, California." *Journal of American Folklore,* Vol. 54 (1941), pp. 24ff.

Jones, Louis C., "The Ghosts of New York: An Analytical Study." *Journal of American Folklore,* Vol. 57 (1944), pp. 237–254.

Kirkland, E. C., "Checklist of Tennessee Folksongs." *Journal of American Folklore,* Vol. 59 (1946), pp. 423ff.

Korson, George, *Pennsylvania Songs and Legends.* Philadelphia, University of Pennsylvania Press, 1949.

Kroeber, A. L., *Handbook of the Indians of California.* Bureau of American Ethnology Bulletin 78, Washington, 1925.

Laws, G. Malcolm, *Native American Balladry.* Philadelphia, American Folklore Society, 1950.

Bibliography

Leach, Maria, Topics and notes in personal folklore and linguistic archives.

———, and Fried, Jerome, *Standard Dictionary of Folklore, Mythology, and Legend,* 2 vols. New York, Funk & Wagnalls Co., 1949–1950.

The Life of Davy Crockett by Himself. New York, New American Library, 1955. Reprinted from *The Life of Davy Crockett,* Philadelphia, 1889, which was a one-volume edition of *A Narrative of the Life of David Crockett, of the State of Tennessee* (1834), *An Account of Col. Crockett's Tour to the North and Down East* (1835), and *Col. Crockett's Exploits and Adventures in Texas* (1836).

Linscott, E. H., *Folk Songs of Old New England.* New York, The Macmillan Co., 1939, pp. 26–30, 44–46.

Lomax, John A. and Alan, *Cowboy Songs and Other Frontier Ballads.* New York, The Macmillan Co., 1938.

Loomis, C. Grant, "Tall Tale Miscellany, 1830–1886." *Western Folklore,* Vol. 6 (1947), pp. 28–41.

———, "Some Lore of Yankee Genius." *Western Folklore,* Vol. 6 (1947), pp. 341ff.

———, "Traditional American Wordplay." *Western Folklore,* Vol. 9 (1950), pp. 147ff.

Lothrop, Samuel Kirkland, *The Indians of Tierra del Fuego.* Museum of the American Indian, Heye Foundation, New York, 1928.

Lowie, Robert H., "The Tropical Forests," *Handbook of South American Indians.* Bureau of American Ethnology Bulletin 143, Vol. 3. Washington, 1948, p. 46.

McKeown, B., "Casey Jones." *Yankee,* Vol. 19 (May, 1955), pp. 38ff.

Métraux, Alfred, *Myths of the Toba and Pilagá Indians of the Gran Chaco.* Memoir 40, American Folklore Society, 1946.

Parsons, Elsie Clews, *Tewa Tales.* Memoir 19, American Folklore Society, 1926, p. 118.

Partridge, Eric, *A Dictionary of Slang and Unconventional English,* 3rd ed. London, Routledge and Kegan Paul, Ltd., 1949.

———, *A Dictionary of the Underworld.* London, Routledge and Kegan Paul, Ltd., 1950.

Pearce, T. M., "The English Proverb in New Mexico." *California Folklore Quarterly,* Vol. 5 (1946), p. 354.

Perrow, E. C., "Songs and Rhymes from the South." *Journal of American Folklore,* Vol. 26 (1913), pp. 142–143.

Pike, R. E., "Folk Songs from Pittsburg, New Hampshire." *Journal of American Folklore,* Vol. 48 (1935), pp. 337ff.

Pound, Louise, "Nebraska Legends of Lovers' Leaps." *Western Folklore,* Vol. 8 (1949), p. 311.

Price, Robert, *Johnny Appleseed, Man and Myth.* Bloomington, Indiana University Press, 1954.

Puckett, N. N., *Folk Beliefs of the Southern Negro.* Chapel Hill, University of North Carolina Press, 1926.

Rasch, P. J., and Mullin, R. N., "Dim Trails—The Pursuit of the McCarty Family." *New Mexico Folklore Record,* Vol. 8 (1954), pp. 8ff.

———, "New Light on the Legend of Billy the Kid." *New Mexico Folklore Record,* Vol. 7 (1953), pp. 4ff.

Robb's Cabinet of Curiosities: A Collection of Interesting, Amusing, and Instructive Clippings Culled from Old Newspapers and Family Scrapbooks, by Robb Sagendorph, Vol. 2. Dublin, New Hampshire, 1952.

Roberts, H., "Louisiana Superstitions." *Journal of American Folklore,* Vol. 40 (1927), pp. 144ff.

Romano, Octavio, "The Clever Mexican." *New Mexico Folklore Record,* Vol. 6 (1951–1952), p. 25.

Bibliography

Sandburg, Carl, *The People, Yes.* New York, Harcourt, Brace & Co., 1936.

Shankle, G. E., *State Names, Flags, Seals, Songs, Birds, Flowers, and Other Symbols.* New York, H. W. Wilson Co., 1934.

Shay, Frank, *A Sailor's Treasury.* New York, W. W. Norton & Company, Inc., 1951.

Shoemaker, Henry W., "Old Boatmen Seek Return of Mike Fink's Body to Pennsylvania." Harrisburg *Capital News,* January 6, 1956.

Skinner, Charles M., *Myths and Legends of Our Own Land,* 2 vols. Philadelphia, J. B. Lippincott Co., 1896.

Speare, Mrs. G. E., *More New Hampshire Folk Tales.* Plymouth, New Hampshire, 1936.

Speck, Frank G., "Some Micmac Tales from Cape Breton Island." *Journal of American Folklore,* Vol. 28 (1915), pp. 59–60.

Stout, Carl J., *Folk-Lore from Iowa.* Memoir 29, American Folklore Society, 1936.

Swanton, John R., *The Indian Tribes of North America.* Bureau of American Ethnology Bulletin 145, Washington, 1953.

———, *Myths and Tales of the Southeastern Indians.* Bureau of American Ethnology Bulletin 88, Washington, 1929.

Teit, James A., *Mythology of the Thompson Indians.* Publications Jesup North Pacific Expedition, Vol. 8, New York, 1912.

United States Federal Writers' Project, *Alabama: A Guide to the Deep South.* New York, Richard R. Smith, 1941.

———, *California, a Guide to the Golden State.* New York, Hastings House, Publishers, Inc., 1943.

Wagley, Charles, *The Social and Religious Life of a Guatemalan Village.* Memoir 71, American Anthropological Association, 1949.

Walton, Ivan H., "Folk Singing on Beaver Island." *Midwest Folklore,* Vol. 2 (1952), pp. 243ff.

Webb, W. Prescott, "Notes on the Folk-Lore of Texas." *Journal of American Folklore,* Vol. 28 (1915), p. 290.

Whitney, A. W., and Bullock, C. C., *Folk-Lore from Maryland.* Memoir 18, American Folklore Society, 1925.

Zunser, Helen, "New Mexican Village." *Journal of American Folklore,* Vol. 48 (1935), pp. 125–178.

Index

About the Author

MARIA LEACH is probably best known as compiler-editor of the distinguished two-volume *Standard Dictionary of Folklore, Mythology, and Legend*—the product of more than twelve years' research. American folklore has long been a special interest of hers—particularly in the areas of dialects, folk speech, and slang—and her love of the subject led to the writing of *The Rainbow Book of American Folk Tales and Legends*. In 1952 Mrs. Leach published her first book for children. Two years later came *The Soup Stone: The Magic of Familiar Things,* and in 1956, *The Beginning: Creation Myths Around the World,* for older children. *God Had a Dog: The Folklore of the Dog* is her most recent book for adults. Mrs. Leach, who lives in New York City and spends her summers in Nova Scotia, is a member of the American Folklore Society, of which she has been a Councillor, the American Anthropological Association, and the French Folklore Society.

About the Artist

MARC SIMONT, winner of the Caldecott Award for the "most distinguished American picture book for children published in 1956," was born in Paris of Spanish parents. He spent his early years in Barcelona, came to the United States as a teen-ager, and after high school returned to Paris to study art. Now an American citizen, he lives in New York City and West Cornwall, Connecticut. Among the well-known authors to whose books he has brought the wit and imaginative vigor of his illustrations are James Thurber, Meindert De Jong, Ruth Krauss, Babette Deutsch, and Elizabeth Lansing; he has also worked with Red Smith and Alistair Cooke and has found time as well for five books of his own.

This book was set in

Baskerville type by

Graphic Services, Incorporated.

It was printed by

Copifyer Lithograph Corporation

on Perkins and Squier Company's Special Offset

made by P. H. Glatfelter Company.

The binding was done at

the press of The World Publishing Company.

Typography and design are by

Lawrence S. Kamp

3 4 5 6 7 8 65 64 63